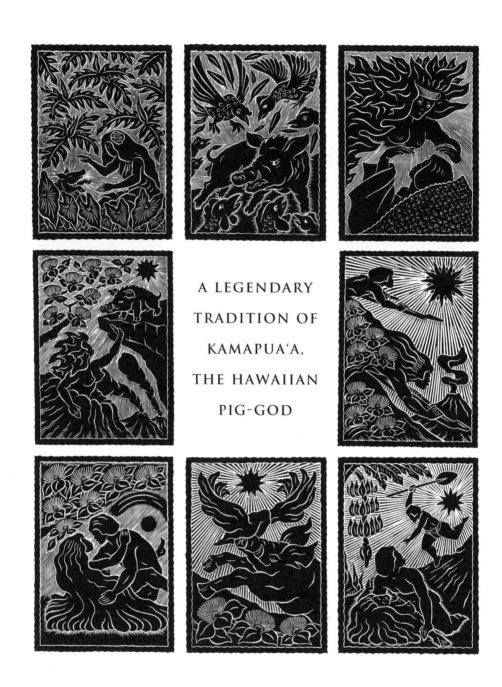

A LEGENDARY
TRADITION OF
KAMAPUA'A,
THE HAWAIIAN
PIG-GOD

Illustrated by Dietrich Varez

HE MOʻOLELO
KAʻAO O
KAMAPUAʻA

An Annotated Translation of
a Hawaiian Epic from
KA LEO O KA LĀHUI
June 22, 1891–July 23, 1891

LILIKALĀ K. KAMEʻELEIHIWA

Bishop Museum Press

DEDICATION

Ho'ola'a 'ia no ku'u mau keiki hiwahiwa,
'o Nā'ālehu Kilohana Kana'iaupuni lāua
'o Punihei Kaiwipunikauikawēkiu, me ku'u aloha nui.
§♥ For the beloved children Nā'ālehu and Punihei,
with all my love.

To the memory of John Dominis Holt,
a *keiki'eu* decendant of Hanakaulani and Pi'ilani,
and the sage of Kupanihi.

The reprinting of this publication is sponsored by Bishop Museum's
Native Hawaiian Culture and Arts Program in celebration of the Legacy
of Excellence of Native Hawaiian culture. The Legacy of Excellence
volumes are devoted to generating an appreciation of Native Hawaiian
traditions, art, and language through education, awareness, and
recognition of excellence in Native Hawaiian achievement.

The Native Hawaiian Culture and Arts Program (NHCAP) was created
by the U.S. Congress through the American Indian, Alaska Native, and
Native Hawaiian Culture and Arts Development Act (Higher Education
Amendments of 1986, P.L. 99-498). It was implemented in 1987 upon
the execution of the first cooperative agreement between the National
Park Service and Bishop Museum. NHCAP is dedicated to making a
meaningful and continuing contribution to the well-being of Native
Hawaiian people through the perpetuation and growth of Native
Hawaiian language, culture, arts, and values.

Bishop Museum Press Special Publication 89

ISBN 0-930897-60-9
Library of Congress Catalog No.93-74559

Printed in the United States of America

Text design and production by Barbara Pope Book Design

CONTENTS

INTRODUCTION

The epic of Kamapua'a, the Hawaiian pig-god, is a wonderful example of the grand tradition of Hawaiian orature, which flourished for thousands of years in *Hawai'i nei*, and in other parts of Polynesia before that. Orature is an art form that all Polynesians excel in, and one that continues to delight modern Hawaiians. Stories of mythological beings from the beginning of time, Gods and Goddesses, and explanations of the cosmos are, of course, not unique to Hawai'i or Polynesia. Everywhere myths abound, and to the extent that they are remembered and recounted in any society, they inspire and shape that society's cultural identity.

In the West, fairy tales of damsels in distress rescued by handsome young princes, preferably rich, play a role in shaping the expectations that women and men have about their relationships. The role of Hawaiian mythology is not dissimilar, but the motifs are vastly different, especially with respect to sexuality. With forty thousand *Akua*, or Gods, represented by many varied aspects of nature, and with the continual mating of the earth-mother and sky-father, the world of traditional Hawai'i was complex in its symbolic meanings, and in its celebration of lovemaking. It was completely different from the Western society that exists in Hawai'i today. As modern Hawaiians seek to reestablish our sovereignty, these grand epics of our ancestors thrill us with new accounts of ancient heroes and heroines who are distinctly Hawaiian. For the non-Hawaiian, myths such as this legend of Kamapua'a provide an understanding of those aspects of Hawaiian society not yet forgotten, but seldom heard.

It is not by accident that Hawaiian epics are generally unknown to us. After contact with Western diseases, beginning in 1778, Hawaiians experienced massive depopulation, at least 80 percent in the first fifty years of contact. By 1891, when this legend of Kamapua'a was published, only forty thousand Hawaiians, or 5 percent of the original native population, remained (Stannard 1989:30; Schmitt 1968:41, 74). With such a rapid decline in numbers, many of the old traditions were lost forever. Even more detrimental to the maintenance of Hawaiian literature has been the past one hundred years of American colonialism and the banning of Hawaiian language. As Hawaiian children were beaten over two generations for the sin of speaking Hawaiian, Hawaiian-language newspapers and books ceased to be published. Access to such traditions became severely limited. Today Hawaiians disagree with such colonial notions and seek to uncover and celebrate our great traditions.

The grand epics that remain, like Kamapua'a, or Pele and Hi'iaka, Lā'ie-ikawai or Kū-a-pāka'a, coupled with an impressive array of poetry and short story, give us a tantalizing glimpse of the ancient Hawaiian world. While we wish there were more, we have yet to finish exploring what we have. Much of Hawaiian orature has long been locked away in musty university libraries and museums or lain dormant on reels of microfilmed Hawaiian-language newspapers, generally inaccessible to the public. Fortunately for the modern reader, Hawaiians began publishing their epics and poetry in Hawaiian-language newspapers, beginning in the 1830s, almost as soon as writing was introduced, thereby preserving these treasures for future generations.

The Hawaiian population has happily recovered to a comfortable 200,000, and we are eager to seek out and share with the world the literary gifts bequeathed by our ancestors. Accordingly, Bishop Museum Press is publishing this annotated translation of a portion of the Kamapua'a epic, which has long been buried in the Hamilton Library microfilm collection at the University of Hawai'i.

"He Mo'olelo Ka'ao o Kamapua'a" ("A Legendary Tradition of Kamapua'a") was published in 1891 in *Ka Leo o ka Lāhui*, (literally, "The Voice of the Nation"), a popular Hawaiian-language daily newspaper. The epic was sixty-seven chapters long and ran from June 22, 1891, through September 28, 1891. Presented here are the first twenty-two chapters, one-third of the story; the latter parts await translation.

One hundred years before the published version of this epic was available, Hawaiians in 1791, without television, radio, or video machines, would have whiled away their evening hours recounting epics such as this one, which is replete with fantastic heroes, a complicated plot, and beautiful renditions of chant and *hula*, interspersed with clever proverbs. In orature, the artistic telling of the epic was as important as the story itself, and the modern reader has to provide the theater of the original production with the imagination. The raconteur would take many hours and certainly many successive nights to present such an epic to an eager audience of *Ali'i Nui,* or high chiefs, as well as to *maka'āinana,* or commoners. In traditional Hawai'i, everyone enjoyed and participated in the arts, ensuring a greater knowledge of the finer aspects of life by the general population than is commonly found in modern American society.

Hawaiian poetry and narrative were critically judged by their audience as sophisticated or simple, depending on the levels of *kaona,* or hidden meanings, presented. The sexual metaphors in this version of the Kamapua'a epic are striking, and can prove problematic to a translator. Most English translations have failed to capture the subtlety and emotional nuances (especially sexual nuances) of the original, which were so dear to the hearts of Hawaiian audiences. This problem was extensively discussed by Beckwith in her introduction to *Laieikawai* (1919:294–96), but was never completely resolved. My solution has been to translate as literally as possible, providing extensive annotation of each pertinent metaphor.

In the highly developed art of Hawaiian storytelling, there are always several levels of *kaona* in any good example of Hawaiian prose. There is the tale at its face value; boy meets girl, falls in love, falls out of love, and so on. An additional level is introduced by innumerable allusions to ancient events, myths, Gods, and chiefs that have become metaphors in their own right. This includes the use of place names and the symbolism attached to the names of winds, rains, plants, and rocks, evoking a certain emotional quality on many levels (Luomala 1965:235–47; Elbert 1976:117–32).

Chants and proverbs enhance the story with an additional shade of meaning as they, too, are interpreted on their surface value and also refer to a more ancient time and perhaps more profound event for which they were originally composed. There may even be a fourth level, conveyed by the manner in which the story is told, known only to the raconteur and one or two special members of the audience, perhaps a lover or close friend, while everyone else remains oblivious to the message.

These subtle levels of meaning are like strands of a *lei* woven together as an object of honor and affection for loved ones and the *Ali'i Nui*. Their function is to remind the audience of something that is similar to the present topic and at the same time slightly different. This device not only creates a certain mood but adds to the beauty of the work, as what is seen on the surface can be interpreted simultaneously on other levels.

An example of *kaona* is illustrated by the word *mahiki*. *Mahiki* means "to jump, leap, hop, move up and down, vibrate" (Pukui-Elbert 1971). It is a term used in *mele ma'i*, or genital chants, to describe sexual motions. It is also famous as a place name on the Hāmākua coast of Hawai'i Island, where Kamapua'a chanted a teasing love song about a love affair (Kahiolo 1978: 74–77). Thus, whenever the term *mahiki* is used, one is reminded of the meaning of the word, in everyday and sexual use, and of the place called Mahiki that was poetically connected with love affairs.

Just who was this Kamapua'a (literally, pig-child) and what role did he play in traditional Hawai'i? How is it that a pig, a symbol of filth and gross behavior in the West, became such a hero in Hawai'i? Were pig-heroes a common motif in Polynesia, and is he an ancient symbol? What is his place in Hawaiian orature and myth?

Kamapua'a, the Hawaiian Pig-God, is that ancient creature who roots in the deep black mud of the cool forest. He is that *Akua* who changes his body form at will; now a beautiful and virile youth, tempting women, and then a giant boar ruthlessly devouring his terrified enemies. Sometimes he is a *nukunuku-ā-pua'a* fish cowering in the sea, fleeing the burning wrath of Pele's lava, and then he becomes a *kukui* tree or a clump of *'uhaloa* grass, silently hiding from his enemies in the forest.

Defiant of all authority, bold and untamed, he recalls the pig nature that lies dormant in most people. He is the primeval reveler, lusting after life; he is the creature eagerly suckling at a mother's breast. Treacherous and tender, he thirsts greedily after the good things in life—adventure, love, and sensual pleasure. Kamapua'a is a hero to Hawaiians because he recognizes no societal restraint, and we love him for it.

Mischievous and audacious, he suffers no retribution and he acknowledges no pressing responsibilities. He has a deep affection for his family, but he rarely stays at home. He falls madly in love with beautiful women and becomes their ardent companion, but soon finds new adventures awaiting him elsewhere. He faces terrifying opponents with an eager but nonchalant attitude, impressing his audience with his bravery. When he inevitably defeats the local champion, he seeks no glory or power, for that would imply responsibility and duty. Instead, he gaily proceeds to another episode in a new territory, seeking a fresh challenge with which to amuse himself.

The pig-ancestor first appears in the fifth epoch of the creation of the world as described in the *Kumulipo* (Beckwith 1972:200, line 490), a creation chant composed as a cosmogonic genealogy, unfolding from the beginning of time and continuing to the sixteenth epoch (the eighteenth century), when *Ali'i Nui* ruled the Hawaiian Islands. In the *Kumulipo*, Hawaiian time begins with darkest night, the ancient female ancestor, who gives birth to male and female nights. Brother and sister mate in an incestuous union to produce the divinity of the universe, which is all life. They give birth to the coral polyp in the fundamental slime of the earth; each creature in its turn gives birth to other sea creatures and seaweeds, proceeding up the evolutionary chain through the fish, birds, and creeping things until at last the pig is born:

'O ke kama a pua'a i hānau
The pig-child is born

Ho'ohale uka i ka nāhelehele
Lodging inland in the bush

Ho'omaha i ka lo'ilo'i o Lo'iloa
Cultivates the water taro patches of Lo'iloa

'O 'umi he au ka moku
Tenfold is the increase of the island

'O 'umi he au ka 'āina
Tenfold the increase of the land

495   *Ka 'āina a Kapōkanokano i noho ai*
The land where the Night-digger dwelt

'Ōli'uli'u ke ala i ma'awe nei
Long is the line of his ancestry

'O ka ma'awe hulu hiwa o ka pua'a
The ancient line of the pig of chief blood

. . . .

Laha ai kama o Lo'iloa
531   The children of Lo'iloa multiplied

'O ululoa ka 'āina o Mohala
The virgin land sprang into bloom

E ku'u mai ana i ka ipu makemake
The gourd of desire was loosened

'O ka makemake kini peleleu.
With the desire to extend the family line.

(Beckwith 1972:82–84, 199–201)

From the *Kumulipo* we see that Kamapua'a is of ancient ancestry, associated from the earliest time with the planting of taro and with the fertility of the land and his human descendants, who worshiped him. As an ancestor he became an *Akua* of taro farmers and was associated with the fertility *Akua* Lono (Beckwith 1970:210–11), as one of Lono's earthly manifestations. An altar of stones topped by a carved pig's head marked the boundary of each district (Pukui-Elbert 1971, *ahupua'a*) upon which first-fruit Makahiki offerings were collected for Lono (Malo 1951:146). In Hāmākua, Hawai'i, worshipers of Kamapua'a would place a newborn child's navel in the mouth of the pig's head image to ensure the child would grow up as a farmer, as the *kumu hula* John Kaʻimikaua often recounts (lecture, 1979).

While worshiped by some as one of the forty thousand *Akua*, most Hawaiians agreed that Kamapuaʻa was of that mysterious and powerful class of beings known as *kupua* (Beckwith 1970:201). *Kupua* were people "of extraordinary powers of body or mind" (Andrews 1974:319), who could magically shift from human form to animal, plant, or rock forms, as their nature or will dictated. Thus, there were shark *kupua*, rock *kupua*, dog *kupua*, bird *kupua*, and pig *kupua*; their powers differed according to the nature of their form. They were often the *ʻAumākua*, family Gods or ancestral guardians, of both *makaʻāinana* and *Aliʻi Nui*, reflecting the familial relationship between the classes.

The two principal body forms that Kamapuaʻa often assumed were those of a handsome young man and a pig; the latter was either a very large or very little pig (Beckwith 1970:202). As a human he excelled in making love to women, and as a pig he was best at making mischief. Like most epic heroes he succeeded in all his endeavors.

Nowhere else in Polynesia is there evidence that a pig was worshiped as a God (Kirtley 1971:115–17), and some maintain that nowhere else was devotion to sensual pleasure so exalted and refined as in Hawaiʻi (Ellis 1782 v. 2:153, in Sahlins 1981:39). There have been no other *Akua* named Kamapuaʻa; there is none other quite like him. His ancestors are said to have come from Kahiki, or Tahiti (Beckwith 1970:201), but he was born at Kaluanui, a district on the windward side of Oʻahu.

The legend of Kamapuaʻa begins with the hero's genealogy, for his lineage defines his character. In particular, the incestuous behavior of his ancestors, according to one elderly Hawaiian gentleman, Papa Kalāhikiola Naliʻiʻelua (guest lecture, 1979), was a direct cause of his pig form, as well as his excessive sexual adventures. Kamapuaʻa was descended from Māui and Oʻahu chiefly lineages, and one of his female ancestors was Haumealani, a Tahitian Goddess. Although he was raised as a commoner, he was able to perform great feats because of his exalted lineage. Hawaiians of traditional times, as well as the readers of the 1891 *Ka Leo o ka Lāhui* newspaper, would have suspected a chiefly lineage of such a hero, even had it not been presented, and the author does not disappoint his audience.

However noble, the family of Kamapuaʻa fell from grace in a comedy of errors, leaving them more destitute than the most common *makaʻāinana*. The setting of the story is the rain-swept windward district of Oʻahu, and early in the plot the scene is set for Kamapuaʻa to rise from the most humble beginnings to the greatest heights. Although born as a younger brother in a society that imbues the eldest child with special *mana*, or spiritual power, he becomes a great taro planter and the principal provider for his family. All of his wondrous feats are due to the *mana* of his grandmother (which in many ancient Polynesian epics is a natural source of wisdom).

It is only after his family is well fed and comfortable that he begins his mischievous adventures. He tempts fate and the wrath of the *Ali'i Nui* of O'ahu with his chicken-stealing exploits. The *kaona* of this episode are many: maka-'āinana rising against *Ali'i Nui*, a junior lineage prevailing over the senior lineage, and a contest of *mana* between *pua'a* (pig) and *moa* (chicken) *'Aumākua*, the latter of whom was worshiped by 'Olopana, the *Ali'i Nui* of O'ahu and archenemy of Kamapua'a.

Once Kamapua'a becomes the champion of O'ahu and has risen to *Ali'i Nui* status, he seeks to escape from *Ali'i Nui* responsibilities. Not for him is the ruling of a kingdom and seeing to the welfare of the people. Instead, he assumes his fish body and swims away to a foreign land for a few adventures with Tahitian chiefesses. It is also at this time that he first assumes his human form, as if Kamapua'a could only become a handsome young man once he has proven himself equal to an *Ali'i Nui*.

In Tahiti, the land of his divine female ancestor, one supposes that Kamapua'a might find true conjugal bliss, conquering a local hero and sleeping with two sisters. As before when he became the greatest taro farmer, or the most daring warrior, life becomes boring when there is no challenge, and he is only momentarily satisfied. The same is true of his love affairs. In almost every village through which Kama (as he is affectionately known) travels, a woman emerges to eagerly offer up her charms. When he sometimes refuses out of boredom, the women are most offended. Did such behavior normally provoke female indignation in ancient Hawaiian society? Perhaps. In any event, he leaves his Tahitian sweethearts with excuses of supernatural demands from a dream lover.

His encounter with Pele is the most dramatic of all the episodes and is filled with impressive oratory by way of lengthy chants. The *kaona* of the event has many levels. Their relationship proceeds like the proverbial war between the sexes, with each side striving to dominate the other. On another level their affair represents the eternal struggle between the desolation of Pele's burning lava and the wet, lush growth represented by the impregnating element of Kamapua'a. Hawaiian lava makes for incredibly fertile soil, and once the winter rains make it cool, fresh green ferns spring up in the "virgin land," as we learned in the *Kumulipo*.

Like many of the Hawaiian female *Akua*, Pele is a powerful and dominating woman, who usually chooses for lovers men who submit to her wishes and demands. While not quite an *Akua* of the same *mana* as Pele, Kamapuaʻa has usually been the dominant partner in his previous relationships. He is excited by Pele because of the challenge she represents. He comes to the volcano at Kīlauea to awaken Pele's desires.

The volcanic pit is symbolically Pele's vagina, and she is insulted that he has come to stand at the crater's edge without her invitation. She denounces him as a pig, and Kamapuaʻa is ashamed of his true nature. Pele promises he will die (or be defeated) for attempting to violate her sacred mountain, and when he nearly escapes, she is so indignant that she offers him an irresistible lure in order to continue the fight. I will not tell you the outcome of their encounter and spoil your enjoyment of the tale, but remember that while their struggle was probably played out between Hawaiian men and women on a daily basis, it was also part of a competition of *mana* between Oʻahu and Hawaiʻi Island *Akua*.

Survey of the Literature

Once Hawaiians learned the miracle of writing, a literary tradition arose that reflected their traditional love of orature. People from every class and background, and with varying degrees of eloquence, seemed compelled to write down what they knew, and often challenged the opinions of fellow Hawaiians in heated letter-writing debates.

From 1834 to 1948, there were dozens of Hawaiian-language newspapers, which unlike their English counterparts, consistently published epics and poetry, because their Hawaiian audience preferred reading works of literature to the latest news of the world. Epics were almost always front-page copy, while news and business items were tucked inside on page 2 or 3. Because of their enthusiasm, we have thousands of pages of Hawaiian literature on microfilm, virtually untouched and without even a subject index.

With such diversity, it is surprising that, besides this 1891 version of the Kamapuaʻa epic, only two other versions have survived and are well known today, although there have been a number of English versions of the Kamapuaʻa legend. Perhaps other accounts await discovery, as scholars read their way through the Hawaiian-language microfilms.

An early version of the story was collected by Abraham Fornander in the mid-1800s and published along with his three-volume work, *Collection of Hawaiian Antiquities and Folklore* (1916–1919). The other was written by G. W. Kahiolo for a weekly newspaper, *Ka Hae Hawaiʻi,* in 1861. Subsequently, the Kahiolo text was extracted and translated by Esther Moʻokini and Erin Neizman and published by the Hawaiian Studies Program at the University of Hawaiʻi in 1978. All three Hawaiian versions agree on main points in the story, but with varied emphasis on different themes.

Fornander's version gives much attention to the warlike nature of Kamapuaʻa and his superhuman strength. Great battles are waged against impossible odds, from which he never fails to emerge victorious. The story is narrated in rather somber chants, with short spurts of prose to introduce them, which seems to leave the audience to fill in the details. Even his famous lovemaking episode with Pele is described as a battle rather than a seduction; his character is portrayed as a fierce and temperamental *Akua.*

The Kahiolo version, on the other hand, paints Kamapuaʻa as a lost soul, constantly in search of his family. Having been born in a strange form—as a piece of cord—his mother rejects and ignores him, and the story of his life is a continual struggle for acceptance and acknowledgment by his family. This too is rather a somber piece, with many long, humorless chants. Humor may have been injected into the oral narrative, but it is absent in print. In this version, Kamapuaʻa, despite his superhuman power, is made to suffer the sad frustrations of the most abject human.

The *Ka Leo o ka Lāhui* version has a completely different tenor and is more extensive than the other two; in this version there are over one hundred chants and proverbial sayings, many of which have sexual connotations and remain unrecorded in other traditional sources. The prose sections are elegant and far more developed than Fornander's, which relies more heavily on the use of chant narrative; this is a tale meant to be read. The chants in this version, although beautiful and complex, are frequently different and more varied than those usually quoted in the previous versions. Chants from the Pele and Hiʻiaka epic (Emerson 1909) are included, as well as a name chant for Pauahi, an *Aliʻi Nui* who died in 1886.

As in earlier versions, Kamapuaʻa travels from Oʻahu to Tahiti and back, moving up the island chain from Hawaiʻi to Kauaʻi, but in this story there is charming attention to detail, and amusing exchanges between characters. Here we witness not only his famous battles, but also his bedroom conversations. Where before we heard of his lovemaking with various women, here we are made privy to his very speeches of seduction.

Because "A Legendary Tradition of Kamapuaʻa" had such an expressly sexual theme and was printed at a time when moral standards were set by the Calvinists, one wonders whether any *haole* (whites) could read Hawaiian then or whether any bothered to read *Ka Leo o ka Lāhui*. I can well imagine this version being condemned as pornography, as had King Kalākaua's 1883 coronation program, which printed the titles of *mele maʻi*, genital chants, performed in his honor. However, there seems to have been no notice made of Kamapuaʻa in the English-language newspapers.

Since it is so full of metaphor that would have been understood and enjoyed by the readers of *Ka Leo o ka Lāhui* in 1891, we know something of the level of Hawaiian literary culture at that time. Because it is not a simple recounting of a memorized story, as would have been told orally, but rather a reworked version meant to be eloquent and moving when read, we know that the art of Hawaiian storytelling was alive, changing, and adapting itself to written form in 1891.

This version of the Kamapuaʻa legend is interwoven with a sublime sense of what the Hawaiians call *kolohe* (mischievous, naughty, rascal), and all in a sexual way. *Kolohe* is one of the more valuable aspects of ancient Hawaiian culture that has survived to modern times. Older Hawaiians, especially, still continue to speak and joke in a *kolohe* way, so that talking about "doing it," or making love, the flirting and smirks and sly glances, may be more fun than the act of love itself. The Hawaiian orientation makes the playful imagining as satisfying as the actual lovemaking, because it releases tension and produces laughter and joy (Pukui, Haertig, and Lee 1972:85). Everyone then feels good, not just the couple involved. Traditional Hawaiians considered it psychologically very healthy to treat the act of sex as a funny, open, and human event. There should be no guilt or enforced secrecy about sex from this point of view. There was no pretense that sex never happened, as was the proffered ideal of Calvinist Christianity so dominant in Hawaiʻi in 1891.

The prose in the 1891 version glorifies the sexual propensities of men and women in the same manner that *mele maʻi*, genital chants, do in poetry. The prowess and excesses of Kamapuaʻa in lovemaking were attributed to his fundamental pig nature; he was eternally attracted to the female element. In the Hawaiian way of thinking, the pig's snout was a phallic symbol, rooting in the wet mud of the female earth. Wetland taro patches were symbolic of female genitalia and the female reproductive capacity. Hence, the rooting (*ʻeʻeku*) of pigs was also seen as a sexual metaphor, and the subject elicited much laughter in the Hawaiian audience.

The expressly sexual theme of the 1891 version of the Kamapuaʻa epic was presented at a time when Hawaiians were rejecting *haole* rules in the cultural and political spheres of life. King Kalākaua had revived *hula* as a genuine form of Native entertainment, and encouraged Hawaiians to enjoy the traditional Hawaiian celebration of love affairs. Calvinists were most upset by the "recrudescense of heathenism" (Alexander 1896:1). It is interesting to note that historically, in the early rebellions of "pagan" chiefs against Christian chiefs (1829, 1831, 1833–1834), one of the most blatant outward manifestations of disrespect was the public performance of the *kolohe hula* (Sahlins 1981:65–66). Was perhaps the *Ka Leo o ka Lāhui* account a *kolohe* tradition in rebellion against the foreign element as well?

Ka Leo o ka Lāhui was formed by Native Hawaiians who sought to organize the Hawaiian race in support of the king and in opposition to the powerful *haole* business community. Among the newspaper's loyal supporters, that is, those who regularly contributed cash toward its support, were Liliʻuokalani, sister of the king, and J. Nawahī and E. Lilikalani, two Hawaiians prominent in political circles, the latter being King Kalākaua's genealogist.

Ka Leo o ka Lāhui had a large, Native Hawaiian–speaking audience and gained fame for its loyal editorials in support of King Kalākaua and the Hawaiian monarchy. The 1890s were a time of great conflict in Honolulu. The *haole* business and sugar interests had pressed for political changes, and with the 1887 Bayonet constitution, took power from the Hawaiian king and gave it to a *haole* cabinet. The cabinet, of course, was to be comprised of these self-same missionary descendants and business executives who had also demanded closer ties with America in the form of the Reciprocity Treaty or even by annexation (Kuykendall 1967:79–115). Such foreigner settlers had very little concern for what they considered a half-witted, backward, and primitive race (*The Islander* 1875:103, 111–12), and Hawaiians clearly saw the need to organize politically against foreigners who would usurp the Hawaiian crown.

Politics aside, who wrote this version of Kamapuaʻa? That seems to be a mystery, for although it was a popular story, the author was not identified. However, it was common practice in Hawaiian-language dailies to publish regular fictional features anonymously. This was perhaps due to a natural reluctance on the part of Hawaiians to claim as their own a story composed in the distant past and handed down through generations.

And, in fact, those Hawaiians who recorded the ancient oral narratives were not authors in the strict sense of the word. They had not composed these ancient legends, but merely remembered them and wrote them down

as they had heard them. They were antiquarians, recorders of the old traditions that had been created and memorized by the *kākā'ōlelo*, (literally, "to
fence with words"). The *kākā'ōlelo* had been the orator, storyteller, and coun-
selor of the *Ali'i Nui*. The dilemma of the Hawaiian writer in 1891 was that he
could not refer to himself as a *kākā'ōlelo*, an exalted position that had long
since disappeared, nor could he name himself as the author, since he was not.

In most cases, the Hawaiian chose anonymity as the polite solution to this
paradox. Not disclosing oneself as the author was also a way of deflecting
criticism on the veracity of the account. This is very clear from reading the
first issue of the Kamapua'a epic, where the author makes the disclaimer that
perhaps "the exact version is not known today" (June 22, 1891). However,
there are clues to some possible authors.

On January 5, 1893, *Ka Leo o ka Lāhui* began publication of a lengthy serial of *Pele and Hi'iaka*, to which John E. Bush and S. Pa'aluhi appended their
names. The introductory paragraph of *Pele and Hi'iaka* is almost identical to
the opening remarks of *Kamapua'a*, and the writing styles are very similar.
There is no proof that Bush and Pa'aluhi wrote Kamapua'a, but it seems
likely to me.

While not much is known about Pa'aluhi, Bush led an interesting public
life and occupied a number of important positions; he was a member of the
Privy Council from 1878 to 1891; commissioner of Crown Lands and president of the Board of Health in 1880; a member of the House of Nobles from
1880 to 1886; minister of finance and minister of the interior in 1882; envoy
extraordinary to Sāmoa during Kalākaua's bid for a Pacific empire in 1886;
governor of Kaua'i in 1887; and elected representative from O'ahu in 1890–
1892.

In 1888, he became president of Hui Kālai'āina, an organization also
known as the Hawaiian Political Association (Kuykendall 1967:448); and he
was the editor of two Hawaiian-language newspapers, *Ka 'Oia'i'o (The
Truth)* from 1889 to 1896, and *Ka Leo o ka Lāhui* in 1891 and in 1894. He led
many public rallies in support of the king and in opposition to the foreign
business-missionary faction. A man dedicated to his nation, he exhorted
Hawaiians to guard against foreign manipulation.

After Bush (a *hapa*-Hawaiian equally fluent in Hawaiian and in English)
became the editor of *Ka Leo o ka Lāhui*, he began to run the Kamapua'a serial as the front-page lead story. It seems that most Hawaiians, like many people today, tried to avoid politics whenever possible. The Kamapua'a epic was

published in order to get them to buy the paper, and once they did, perhaps they would read Bush's feisty political editorials on the inside pages.

Hawaiians have passed down the tale of Kamapuaʻa from one generation to another, changing minor details to suit their purposes and adding new anecdotes of their own to the list of his adventures. Only a few years ago, a sighting of Kamapuaʻa was reported in confidence to me by some Hawaiians from Hauʻula who were pig hunting in the mountains behind Kaluanui. They were certain it had been Kamapuaʻa because the pig had been enormous, and even though they had shot him in the head and in the buttocks, he did not even pause, but ran quickly past them. Nor did the pig's wounds bleed at all.

The pig ran at a terrific pace down a muddy trail, and the hunters gave chase. They followed his tracks to a barbed-wire fence, at which point his hoofprints disappeared completely. The hunters searched the surrounding area and found nothing, not a hoofprint, not a trampled or broken plant, nor a trace of blood. It was this sudden and rather disconcerting disappearance of what had seemed a very real pig that convinced my friends that they had encountered Kamapuaʻa. When I suggested that he had probably assumed the form of a *kukui* tree, one of his known body forms, explaining how he had vanished so completely, they thought it a likely answer. In any case, this anecdote shows us how real and exciting the idea of Kamapuaʻa continues to be today.

Whether it was Bush, Paʻaluhi, or some other Hawaiian who was the mysterious author of our story, that person was possessed of a fine literary capacity, and "A Legendary Tradition of Kamapuaʻa" proves him, or her, a true scholar of Hawaiian antiquity. The author knew many of the lengthy chants traditional to the Kamapuaʻa epic, the intricate story line, and the appropriate usage of place names and wise sayings to enhance the depth of the legend, as well as the traditional stratagems employed by the Hawaiian raconteur, which in the old days would keep the audience spellbound all night. Now, one hundred years later, we present *He Moʻolelo Kaʻao o Kamapuaʻa* once again to the reading public, and we trust that you will be amused by the tale of this *kolohe* Kamapuaʻa.

L. K. KAMEʻELEIHIWA

ABBREVIATIONS

AP   Andrews-Parker Dictionary, 1922

For. Col.   *Fornander Collection of Hawaiian Antiquities and Folk-Lore,* 1916–1920, volumes IV, V, VI

LAD   Lorrin Andrews Dictionary, 1865

ON   *'Ōlelo No'eau,* 1983

PED   Pukui-Elbert Dictionary, 1971

PN   *Place Names of Hawaii,* 1974

PSIC   Pacific Science Information Center place-name file, Bishop Museum

SO   *Sites of Oahu,* 1978

THE GENEALOGY
AND FAMILY ORIGINS
OF KAMAPUA'A

ISSUE 1

1 THE PIG-CHILD OF KAHIKIʻULA AND HINA—
THE PIG-GRANDCHILD OF KAMAUNUANIHO—
ALSO THE OPPONENT OF PELE, THE WOMAN
OF THE VOLCANO AT KĪLAUEA, AND ALL OF
HIS STORY UNTIL, AT LAST, HE PASSED ON TO
THE ANCESTORS AT THE PILLARS OF KAHIKI.[1]

2 *O ʻoe ia e Haunuʻu, e Haulani*
It is you, O Haunuʻu,[2] O Haulani[3]

E Haʻalokuloku
O Haʻalokuloku[4]

Ka Manō, e ka Iʻa nui
The shark, the big fish

E Uʻi, e Uilani
O Uʻi,[5] O Uilani[6]

Kou inoa Puaʻa ia, e ō mai.
This is your pig name chant—answer!

3 [An explanation]. . . . This is perhaps a story
of a supernatural *kupua,* and it may be puzzling
to the thoughts of some people. It is a tale that
your author shall publish as a serial before the
friends who read the newspaper *Ka Leo o ka
Lāhui.* It is concerning this pig-man so won-
drously born . . . and indeed, who became an
Akua for a portion of this nation of Hawaiians
who worshiped him in the ancient times. The
story tells of his ancestors, his parents, his birth,
and his matchless strength.

4 If the reader should see any mistakes or blem-
ishes in this story, please forgive me, for while
this story may not be perhaps exactly like those
versions that other people may remember these
days, perhaps there is not a person living at this
time who knows exactly the things that were
done so long ago in the distant past. The exact
correct version is not known today.

5 Kananananuiʻaimoku,[7] a man, lived with Haumealani,[8] a woman, the daughter from Kuʻaihe-
lani,[9] from the Pillars of Kahiki.[10]

1. The short capitalized synopsis
of the story in paragraph 1 and
the name chant in paragraph 2
are repeated in the same manner
at the beginning of every issue,
as if to summon the reader and
the pig-god to the story. I present
them only here in Issue 1. Also, the
word consistently used in the title
until July 15, 1891, is *molelo,* a misspelling of *moʻolelo,* "story, tale,
history, tradition" (PED).

2. *Haunuʻu Lit.,* "elevated
ruler" (PED 382). Although in this
story she is said to be a sister of
Kamaunuaniho, other versions
do not identify her as such. She
is invoked in the name chant of
Kamapuaʻa as an *ʻAumakua,* or
divine ancestor deity of his. Also
found in other name chants for
Kamapuaʻa (For. Col. 6:516, 517;
Kahiolo 1978:23, 97).

3. *Haulani Lit.,* "to root, as a
hog; to plunge as a canoe . . . to be
restless in one's grasp; to squirm . . .
uneasy; seeking freedom from
restraint" (LAD). Said here to be
a brother of Kamaunuaniho, but
perhaps was also an *ʻAumakua* of
Kamapuaʻa. Often chanted in conjunction with Haunuʻu (For. Col.
6:516, 517; Kahiolo 1978:23, 97). It
certainly describes the innate character of Kamapuaʻa—restless and
squirming.

4. *Haʻalokuloku Lit.,* "to pour,
as rain; to disturb; agitated" (PED).
Said here to be a brother of
Kamaunuaniho, and also an
ʻAumakua. A variant, Kaʻaloku-
loku, was called upon in conjunction with Haunuʻu and Haulani in other Kamapuaʻa name
chants (For. Col. 6:516, 517;
Kahiolo 1978:23, 97).

5. *Uʻi Lit.,* a handsome youth,
as Kamapuaʻa often was at times.
This may in fact be *ui,* to question,
as newspapers often omitted the
glottal in print.

6. *Uilani Lit.,* "to chafe under
control; restless, irritated by

restraint; constantly seeking pleasure" (PED). That line could well read "Oh handsome youth, oh restless one." Because this is a name chant for Kamapua'a, intoning these names could be either a plea to his *Akua* for *mana,* or a creation of his character through the power of the spoken word, or both at once.

7. *Kananananui'aimoku* Lit., the great swelling of the ruling chief. The father of Kamaunuaniho by Haumealani, and of Hina, by his own daughter, Kamaunuaniho. Hence, he was the grandfather and great-grandfather of Kamapua'a. In the Hawaiian way of thinking, his name reflected his character, as it was his swollen member that led him into incest with his daughter. Papa Kalāhikiola Nali'i'elua contends that the pig form of Kamapua'a was a result of the piglike behavior on the part of this ancestor. (University of Hawaii lecture, Religion 482B, 1979.)

8. *Haumealani Lit.,* Heavenly Haumea, referring to Haumea, the Polynesian "earth-mother," who is both fertility goddess and patroness of childbirth and of political power (Beckwith 1970:79, 283). Also the mother of many mythical heroes; usually said to be from Kahiki.

9. *Ku'aihelani* "The name of the cloud land adjoining earth and is the land most commonly named in visits to the heavens or to lands distant from Hawai'i" (Beckwith 1970:78). I spell it with the glottal, as it is pronounced that way in the chant "Ku'aihelani Ka Hali'a la," a dance that is *kapu* to the family of Pi'ilani Lua (Hālau o Waimea) and one that has been performed from at least the 1860s.

10. *Kūkulu o Kahiki* "Pillars of Kahiki; it was believed that the sky was supported by a vertical wall along the horizon" (PED). "That section of the wall that stood over against Kahiki" (Emerson 1909:17).

6   Kananananui'aimoku, the man, was from the cliffs of Kapulehu,[11] close to Waihe'e, Māui.[12] Those were the sands of his birth.

7   Born to Kananananui'aimoku, a man, and to Haumealani, a woman, were these children: Kamaunuaniho[13] [female], Haunu'u [female], Haulani [male], Kamanōkai'anui[14] [male], Lono[15] [male], U'i [male], Uilani [female], Kūliaikekaua[16] [male], and 'Awe'aweikealoha[17] [male]. This concludes the ancestors [or grandparents] of Kamapua'a.

8   Many were the days that Kananananui'aimoku lived with his *wahine* [woman or wife];[18] and from their two loins emerged that group of children whose names were revealed one after the other above.

9   And after that time when their children had been born, their living together as husband and wife became 'worn out'[19] [sexually unexciting], while at the same time their eldest daughter's body grew to maturity, as also did their older children.

10   Kamaunuaniho was raised under a *kapu*,[20] from the time she was very young until she was grown, until it became a suitable time to search for a *kāne* for her.

11   During this time when the father saw that his daughter was at the proper age for a *kāne*, the desire began to grow within him to take their eldest daughter as a second supporting *wahine*.[21]

12   When Haumealani noticed that her *kāne* no longer made love to her, on account of their daughter, she then revealed her thoughts to her *kāne*.

13   But before the *wahine* could bring forth her thoughts, her *kāne* spoke first.

14   "What are your thoughts, my chiefess, you should tell me."

11. *Kapulehu Lit.*, forbidden to the multitudes; here said to be cliffs near Waihe'e, Māui, but it is not found in PN or on Bier's 1976 map, so it may be a place name that has been lost.

12. *Waihe'e, Māui Lit.*, the fleeing water. "Land section, village . . . point, reef, river . . . Wailuku qd." (PN). Māui, "second largest island in the Hawaiian group" (PN), named for the legendary hero, Māui.

13. *Kamaunuaniho Lit.*, a tooth that is used as bait in sorcery. Most famous as the wise and powerful grandmother of Kamapua'a. In another version by Kamakau, Kamaunuaniho came from Kahiki with her father, Kalananu'unuikūamamao, and her mother Humu, and they landed at Kahahawai, Waihe'e, Māui. When Kamaunuaniho became her father's *wahine*, Humu returned to Kahiki (*Kū'oko'a*, January 12, 1867).

14. *Kamanōkai'anui Lit.*, the shark, the big fish. Similar to the third line of name chant for Kamapua'a (paragraph 2, this issue). Later he is called the grandfather of Kamapua'a, probably meaning ancestor, with the connotation of ancestral God. See also For. Col. 6:516, 517; Kahiolo 1978:23, 97.

15. *Lono* Although in this story he is a brother of Kamaunuaniho, he was also one of the four great male *Akua*, the last to come from Kahiki; he is considered an *Akua* of "clouds, winds, the sea, agriculture, and fertility." He had also the form of the pig-man, Kamapua'a" (PED 392). In the Fornander version of Kamapua'a, there was a Lonoike'awe'awealoha, the lovemaking God of Kamapua'a, who made love to Pele's brothers in order to distract them from the battle with Kamapua'a (For. Col. 5:338). See also Kahiolo 1978:65.

16. *Kūliaikekaua Lit.*, striving in war. As a brother of Kamaunuaniho, he is also a grandfather of Kamapua'a. Later in the story he becomes the war *Akua* of Kamapua'a.

17. *'Awe'aweikealoha Lit.*, tentacles of love. A brother of Kamaunuaniho, he is a "grandfather" of Kamapua'a and later his *Akua*. This name has humorous connotations, as the octopus tentacle is likened to a man's penis because of the way it stretches out and shrivels back up again. As the *he'e* lives in the coral reefs, which are female symbols of the body of Hina, it can also squeeze into any crevice or hole. It is not, however, a virile symbol, because the octopus' tentacle never gets stiff and hard, hence the humor.

18. *wahine Lit.*, "woman, lady, wife." (Before the introduction of Christianity in 1820 there was no marriage contract as in the Western sense, beyond the ceremonial first mating of *Ali'i Nui*. After such a mating produced a firstborn child of high lineage, the respective *Ali'i Nui* were free to take any number of partners as their lovers. In traditional Hawai'i, it was all "*moe aku, moe mai*" or sleeping here and there. (Kawaili'ili'i in Kame'eleihiwa 1992:161). Men and woman lived together as *kāne* and *wahine*, but only so long as they enjoyed one another. Hence, my use of the original terms *wahine*, to refer to a female lover of a male, and below, *kāne*, a male lover of a female.

19. *lu'a* "Old and wrinkled, worn and shabby with use, worn-out; sagging, hanging down, flimsy, soft, pliable" (PED). This is a type of sexual pun typical of Hawaiians, as *lu'a* in this case refers to the genitals.

20. *kapu* This word has a great many shades of meaning, and usually all apply at once. Here it means that Kamaunuaniho was raised separately from the general public, that she was taught to carry herself with a particular demeanor and that she would remain a virgin until her parents chose a mate of suitable rank for her. To raise a child under *kapu* was to increase her worth, especially in the eyes of a chief. This practice was common among chiefs but not among commoners. *Lit.*, "taboo, prohibition; special privilege or exemption from ordinary taboo; sacredness; prohibited, forbidden; sacred, holy, consecrated" (PED).

21. *paepae 'ao'ao Lit.*, a side support. Akin in meaning to *iwi 'ao'ao*, "assistant leader in a *hula* troupe." Also *paepae* (PED).

15 His *wahine* replied to him, "Perhaps it would be better for you to take our daughter as a new *wahine* for you."

16 "Then perhaps that decision shall be for the two of us to agree upon, but only if it is deemed proper in your way of thinking," said the *kāne* in reply.

17 "Isn't that then what I have just said? It was I who revealed it to you, that we three should live together."

18 "If that way is good, then we three shall live together as *kāne* and *wāhine*."

19 During this time, while they three were living together, Haumealani had already decided what she was going to do. She would abandon her Hawaiian children, the fruit begotten of their two loins. Her love welled up for her parents, for her family, and for the land of her birth.

20 She prepared everything beforehand in her canoe with enough provisions for an ocean voyage. Together with the help of her divine ancestors of the night, she returned to her motherland with ease, and her canoe departed with her people.

21 At this point in our story, we shall forget Haumealani, and return again to look toward Kananananui'aimoku and Kamaunuaniho's living together.

22 Kamaunuaniho became pregnant and gave birth to Hina,[22] a female. This Hina was raised under a *kapu* by the brothers of Kamaunuaniho, in the uplands of Waihe'e, until she was grown and indeed was filled with matchless beauty. A lovely purity [23] descended like a fragrance upon Hina's physique. Her tender body was constantly drenched by 'the cool bubbling water of Elieli,'[24] which is the famous water of this land.

22. *Hina* Lit., to fall over or from an upright position. In this story she is the daughter of Kamaunua-niho and later the mother of Kamapua'a. Also "probably the most widely known goddess or demigoddess of Polynesia ... frequently connected with the moon" (PED). Hina is often invoked in medicinal prayers in conjunction with Kū, which incidentally means to stand erect. Hina is an *Akua* of reef fishing, while Kū, or Kū'ula, is an *Akua* of deep-sea fishing.

23. *ma'ema'e* This is either a variation or misspelling of *ma'e-ma'e*, "clean, pure, attractive, chaste" (PED).

24. *o ka wai hu'ihu'i o Elieli* Said to be the water of Waihe'e, Māui, which seems to have had peculiar powers to bestow beauty but probably has another, deeper meaning that is not known today. '*Eli'eli* is a term used in many rituals and prayers. *Fig.*, "profound, deep, as a taboo, or its removal" (PED). If Elieli was a place name, it is not found in PN or on Bier's map. *Ka wai ho'iho'i lā'ī o 'Eleile* (the water of 'Eleile that carries back the ti-leaf stalk) (ON 1649). Refers to a water of Māui.

25. *ka maluhia o ke kīhāpai pua* The 'flower garden' is Hina, and her 'serenity' is her virginity (ON 7).

26. *O'ahu* "Most populous of the Hawaiian Islands, 40 miles long, 26 miles wide, with an area of 598 square miles" (PN). A child of Lua and Papa in Hawaiian mythology (Beckwith 1970:302).

27. *'Olopana* Usually cited as the chief of Ko'olau district, O'ahu (For. Col. 5:315; Kamakau, *Ke Au 'Oko'a*, March 31, 1870), who lived in Kailua. Credited with having built five *heiau* in the Kailua district around the twelfth century (SO 218). Here said to be the king of O'ahu and uncle of Kamapua'a. According to Kamakau this

23   When the parents observed the refreshing beauty of their daughter, Kananananui'aimoku had a discussion with his *wahine*-daughter and with the caretakers who had raised their daughter.

24   In their discussion they decided that 'the serenity of this flower garden,'[25] that is, of their favorite child, was *kapu* for the skin of the high chief of the island of O'ahu,[26] that is to say, 'Olopana[27] should free her from this *kapu*.

25   'Olomana,[28] a male, lived with Anini,[29] a female. Born were 'Olopana, a male, and Kahiki'ula,[30] also a male, two royal children, and these were the chiefs of the island of O'ahu.

26   You perhaps should know, O friendly readers of this story, that the parents of 'Olopana were the chiefs of O'ahu in that ancient time.

27   The parents of Hina provided all the things necessary for a sea voyage, for the *kāne*-seeking journey among the people of Ko'olau,[31] to find the one suitable for Hina.

28   Haumealani had left behind a red cane for Kamaunuaniho. This was a cane inherited from Haumealani's ancestors.

29   This cane could change into a canoe sometimes, according to the wishes of its owner, and upon this canoe sailed Kamaunuaniho and her daughter Hina, along with three brothers of Kamaunuaniho—Uilani, Kūliaikekaua, and 'Awe'aweikealoha.

30   There were five in number that set sail from Waihe'e, Māui, in the 'Ole days[32] of the month. Those were the days in which the current flowed away from the land, and so were very good days for ocean traveling.

31   They left behind them their home and family and came in search of a *kāne* for their daughter.

'Olopana also sailed from Kahiki, but was not from Kahiki Bolabola (Borabora). Rather, he was from the part of Kahiki called Keolewa, Haenakulaina, and Kauamoi. His temple was Kawa'ewa'e in Kāne-'ohe, and his younger brother was Kahiki'ula. (*Kū'oko'a*, January 12, 1867.)

28. *'Olomana* Lit., branching hill. Here said to be a chief of O'ahu but not listed on any currently known chiefly genealogy. Kamakau says he was a foreigner who arrived at Mokapu, O'ahu, from some faraway place (Kamakau 1961:325). Also said to have been a great warrior 36 feet tall, who ruled Ko'olaupoko, O'ahu (For. Col. 5:374). When he was killed by Palila, he became the hill of that name in Kailua, O'ahu (SO 235, 236).

29. *Anini* Although here said to be the *wahine* of 'Olomana and mother of 'Olopana, she is not listed on any major genealogy, nor is she named in other versions of the Kamapua'a story. However, there is a place named Keanini, which is an ascent on the Kailua side of a ridge overlooking Waimānalo (SO 238).

30. *Kahiki'ula* Lit., red, or royal, Tahiti. Usually said to be the younger brother of 'Olopana (Kamakau, *Kū'oko'a,* January 12, 1867; Kahiolo 1978:4). Not listed on any chiefly genealogy.

31. *Ko'olau* "Windward sides of the Hawaiian Islands" (PED). Here refers to windward O'ahu.

32. *'Ole* days "Seventh, eighth, ninth, and tenth nights of the moon. . . . Collectively these nights were called *na 'Ole;* they were considered unlucky for fishing, planting, or beginning any important activity because *'ole* also means nothing" (PED). The Hawaiians

32   They set sail on the evening of the day of 'Olekukahi,[33] and in the afternoon of the day of 'Olekulua,[34] their canoe landed at Oneawa.[35]

33   This is the place where Hi'iaka[36] said to her beloved friend, Wahine'ōma'o:[37]

> *'O ku'u Ulukoa i kai o Oneawa*
> O my *koa*[38] grove in the sea of Oneawa,
>
> *E—aloha wale.*
> Only love to you.

34   Wahine'ōma'o disagreed with these words:

35   "You are just lying. Perhaps there in the mountains one sees the *koa* groves, not at the seashore."

36   Perhaps Wahine'ōma'o didn't see the *koa* canoes carried on the shoulders by the men at the seashore of Oneawa.

37   At the time when their canoe landed, the shores of the island of O'ahu were *kapu*. A canoe could not land, because all of the O'ahu shorelines were made *kapu* by the temple consecration of the king, 'Olopana.

38   But this canoe was searching for a place to land, and the people did not suppose that they should be afraid. Meanwhile, guards had been stationed at all the peninsulas of O'ahu, so that if canoes were to land, there should be only death for those people upon them. None were allowed to live, and there would be no *pu'uhonua*[39] to which they could escape.

named each night of the moon and governed their business according to the lunar calendar. Kamaunuaniho should have known, as did the readers of this story, that bad luck would result from her sailing on 'Ole days.

33. *'Olekukahi* "Seventh night of the moon" (PED).

34. *'Olekulua* "Eighth night of the moon" (PED).

35. *Oneawa* "Land division and street, Kailua, O'ahu. Lit., milkfish sand. Oneawa was famous for great quantities of *'ō'io*, and perhaps also awa fish" (PN).

36. *Hi'iaka* There are many Hi'iaka sisters, all sisters of Pele. This Hi'iaka refers to Hi'iaka-i-ka-poli-o-Pele, the youngest and favorite sister, who was sent by Pele to Kaua'i to fetch Pele's lover, Lohi'au. On her way she stopped at Oneawa. An incident from the great Pele and Hi'iaka epic is recalled here.

37. *Wahine'ōma'o* "The companion of Hi'iaka-i-ka-poli-o-Pele on her trip to Kaua'i to fetch Lohi'au for Pele. Lit., green woman" (PED 397). There is more to this name than is known today. She appears in Issue 21 of this story as a companion to Kamaunuaniho at Pu'ukapolei. She seems somehow anciently connected with Pu'u-kapolei, as evidenced in He Mele no Kahahana (For. Col. 6:303).

38. *koa* "The largest native forest trees (*Acacia koa*) . . . formerly used for canoes, surfboards, calabashes" (PED).

39. *pu'uhonua* "In ancient times was an *ahupua'a*, a portion of a district, like Kailua and Wai-kāne for Ko'olaupoko district on O'ahu, and also Kualoa, which was a very sacred land and a true *pu'u-honua*, where persons marked for death were saved if they entered it. . . . The concept of *pu'uhonua* came down from ancient times,

39 On this day when they landed, the guards came to meet with them and gave their *aloha*[40] to these ocean-voyaging visitors.

40 The guards said, "What a pity for you folks. Our king will have to kill you because these are *kapu* days of temple consecration for this king of ours, for 'Olopana."

41 The guards questioned them further. "What sort of canoe do you have? Is it then a royal canoe? And if so, what is the name of the chief?"

42 "Yes, it is a royal canoe, and Hina is the young chiefess aboard this canoe."

43 Kamaunuaniho and her brothers[41] further answered the guards, "What then is the crime for which we should die? Because, indeed, if these are really 'dead bones,'[42] since they are so beautiful to look at, they should die before the king."

44 Here then was the result: They were not to die there, not until the king of O'ahu had viewed the young girl of Māui.

45 So the guards returned before the king, 'Olopana, and displayed this new woman before him. The guards said, "These are two beautiful women with a red canoe.[43] Everything on this canoe is red. There are also three men on board."

and *pu'uhonua* lands had always been observed. They were sacrosanct and inviolable lands; no blood of wrongdoers could be shed once they entered into these *pu'uhonua* lands" (Kamakau 1964:18, 20). Although the concept of *pu'uhonua* was ancient, the area often shifted. Kamakau says that at one time Kailua was one, but not at the time of this story.

40. *aloha* Means "love, affection, compassion . . . greeting, regards" (PED), but it is also a type of greeting in which people who are strangers kiss and embrace each other. It is a moment for sharing love and only good emotions. This is done as a greeting and a farewell. *Aloha* is a term used throughout the text and is usually not translated when it is used with this additional meaning. Moreover, because nonconfrontation was considered polite behavior, should *aloha* not be given upon meeting a stranger, that omission was taken as a nonverbal indication of evil intent.

41. *kaikua'ana* This term actually means "older sibling or cousin of the same sex" (PED), but here it is used to mean brother; it is probably an error, as *kaikunane* would be the correct term.

42. *he mau iwi make* Iwi, or bones, were considered to hold all the *mana* of the human body, so they were used figuratively to mean one's life or one's body.

43. *wa'a 'ula* Lit., red canoe. Most canoes were not red, hence this was a special canoe. In ancient times the color red symbolized that which was sacred or belonging to the *Akua*, and was often used by the chiefs. Hina is here portrayed as a special chiefess, because her canoe and belongings were red.

HINA MEETS KAHIKIʻULA

ISSUE 2

1 Kamaunuaniho said to her brothers, "What shall we do when the king's guards come again and we are taken before 'Olopana?"

2 Kūliaikekaua said, "That's not a problem! And don't you worry about us, we'll just sail off to Kaua'i. There is the land cloud, and where it rests down below, there is a harbor where we can land. 'Cooked taro is the food.'"[1]

3 At this time their sister agreed, and they gave each other their very last *aloha*.

4 We should turn our paths to the correct succession of events[2] in our story.

5 When the guards arrived before the king, he was staying at Puhā.[3] He quickly summoned his priest, that is Kuikui,[4] and the name of his *wahine* was Pāhonu.[5]

6 When the priest arrived before 'Olopana, the king, he asked, "Upon the life of the king, what order should be decreed to me, your servant?"

7 "Here is the decree," said the king. "You have been ordered to come before me this day because a certain canoe from Māui landed yesterday, and there were two women on board the canoe. What is the proper thing to do with these women? Reveal to me your priestly wisdom."

8 "The proper thing is for those women to die. This is the only wisdom that I have to put before you, O King."

9 The eyes of the king were cast down [in thought],[6] and after a while, the eyes were raised up and looked directly before him at Kuikui, his priest, and he answered, "They shall not die. These women shall be saved by the king.

10 "I shall wait until the days of temple consecration are free from *kapu*, and then I shall take[7] these women for myself. I command the people to build a house thatched with leaves[8] for my women to live in."

1. *He mea'ai ia kalo mo'a* Refers to the saying '*ai i kalo mo'a*, to eat cooked taro; figuratively means to enjoy a life of ease (PED, *mo'a*).

2. *kuamo'o* "Road, path"; also as in *kuamo'o 'ōlelo*, "continuous record, history, story, succession of events" (PED). Used here with *alanuihele*, pathway, as a play on words. These are two shades of the same meaning, not actually describing roads, but rather how our mind and thoughts travel down the road of the story.

3. *Puhā* "Stream, Waimānalo, O'ahu. *Lit.*, a hollow (as in a tree)" (PN). This place is famous for the sport of *pu'ewai*, or body surfing, in the fast running water at the mouth of a stream (Cummins 1913:235).

4. *Kuikui Lit.*, "old form for *kukui*, candlenut light (commonly used on Ni'ihau)" (PED). Although he is the high priest of 'Olopana, he is not known from other Kamapua'a versions. Interestingly, *Kukui* is also a place name for a small fishing village in Waimānalo, O'ahu (SO 250).

5. *Pāhonu* In this account, Pāhonu is the *wahine* of Kuikui, 'Olopana's priest. Pāhonu is also the name of a turtle pond near the village of Kukui in Waimānalo, O'ahu (SO 249). *Lit.*, turtle enclosure.

6. *kūlou Lit.*, "to bow the head" (PED). In Hawaiian nonverbal communication, to bow the head means that one is thinking about a problem. When a decision is reached, one raises the head.

7. *ki'i Lit.*, "to fetch, procure, send for, go after, attack; to seek for sexual ends" (PED). *Ki'i* is often used in its double meaning.

8. *halelau* "House thatched with leaves rather than with *pili* grass." Also implies *halelauhau*, "taboo sleeping house for chief and chiefess" (PED).

11   The command of the king was fulfilled. The commoners of Koʻolaupoko united together to build the house.

12   And the priest returned to his house after giving his very last words to the king:

13   "Indeed, in no time the land shall be overcome, taken also by these new women of yours."[9]

14   The king did not heed the words of his priest, because that is the usual nature of kings. So it was, perhaps, with King Kahahana,[10] who did not listen to the teachings of his priest, Kaʻō-pulupulu.[11]

15   The famous words of Kaʻōpulupulu remain with us until this time:

> *I nui ke aho a pā ka ʻili i ke kai,*
> Take a deep breath until you touch the
>   surface of the sea,
>
> *No ke kai hoʻi ua ʻāina.*
> For the sea indeed is this land.[12]

16   When this house was finished, the two women were established in it, while ʻOlopana waited until the time when his temple would be free from *kapu*. Then he would visit the girl of Māui.

17   But when Kahikiʻula, the younger brother of ʻOlopana, heard about these beautiful women, and about the prohibition placed upon their bodies by his elder brother, this younger brother began to think[13] of undoing the sanctity of Hina.[14]

9. *Aʻohe no hoʻi he wā a puni aʻe ka ʻāina, loaʻa ʻē iho nei hoʻi kēia mau wahine hou au* Kuikui's prophecy later comes true, as it is Kamapuaʻa, the son of Hina, who "overcomes the land." Not found in ON.

10. *Kahahana* King of Oʻahu in the late 1700s. A nephew of Kahekili, elected by the Oʻahu council of chiefs to replace his cousin Kūmahana as *Mōʻī*. Because he offended Kahekili, the king of Māui made war upon Oʻahu, killing Kahahana and many Oʻahu chiefs. (Kamakau 1961:128–36; For. Col. 6:282–303.)

11. *Kaʻōpulupulu* Kahahana's wise and loyal *kahuna nui*, or head priest. Kahekili devised a clever scheme to discredit Kaʻōpulupulu in Kahahana's eyes. Because Kahahana believed Kahekili and killed his *Kahuna* Kaʻōpulupulu, he caused his own downfall. (Kamakau 1961:133–40.)

12. This prophecy was made by Kaʻōpulupulu to his son Kahulu-puʻe when they were about to be killed by Kahahana's men. It signified that Kahahana would lose Oʻahu to people from across the sea (For. Col. 6:287; SO 71, 91; Judd 1930:38–39). For an alternate version, see Kamakau 1961:134. Similar to *e nui ke aho, e kuʻu keiki, a moe i ke kai, no ke kai la hoʻi ka ʻāina* (take a deep breath, my son, and lay yourself in the sea, for then the land shall belong to the sea) (ON 363).

13. *naulani* Not listed in PED or LAD. It may perhaps be related to *nau*, "to chew; to gnash with the teeth. . . . To hold in the breath, to restrain one's self from breathing" (LAD).

14. The 'sanctity' (*maluhia*) of Hina refers to her virginity.

18 On a certain evening at twilight, Kahiki'ula and his *kahu*[15] went down by the sea at Oneawa to meet with the strangers, that is, with Hina and her family,[16] with the hope that 'her mountain might be nibbled at.'[17]

19 And so it happened. He actually went down to meet with Hina and her family, with loving thoughts, and indeed there arose within him a desire.

20 And thus they two were joined together on this night, as *kāne* and *wahine,* and so they lived until three nights had passed. And on the fourth night of their sleeping together, Kahiki'ula was truly ensnared by sleep; when he awoke, there was the sun above.[18]

21 He returned to his house and he was seen by a certain young girl. It was she who told 'Olopana that Kahiki'ula and Hina had been joined together.

22 When 'Olopana heard of this improper behavior on the part of his younger brother, he became furious, especially at the thought that these women had been reserved for himself until the days of his temple consecration had passed, when he could then look upon the face of this woman. Here she had already been 'routed'[19] [to satisfy] Kahiki'ula.

23 Therefore, Kahiki'ula and his *wahine,* along with his mother-in-law, were thrown out.

24 Kahiki'ula folks traveled on that very day until they reached Ka'a'awa.[20] There they passed five days.

25 Then 'Olopana, the king, heard that his younger brother, with whom he was so angry, was living nearby with the women.

26 He quickly ordered his men to go forth again and drive out Kahiki'ula folks so that they should live in a distant place. And the command of the king was fulfilled.

15. *kahu* "honored attendant, guardian" (PED). This person was often of the chiefly class, and usually closely related to the high chief he served.

16. *Hina mā Lit.,* Hina folks. A common Hawaiian phrase, and one that will reoccur throughout the story.

17. *e 'aki 'ia mai ana nō kāna mauna* Mauna, or mountain, is a pun on *pu'u,* mound, which is slang for vagina. Not found in ON.

18. The implication is that on the three previous nights, Kahiki-'ula had left before daylight; however, by this oversleeping, their love affair could then become a kind of serious relationship called *ho'āo, lit.,* "until daylight" (PED).

19. *puehu* "Scattered, dispersed, routed, gone; fine crumbling; every which way, as hair in the wind" (PED). A sexual euphemism. This transgression by Kahiki'ula was extremely serious because under the strict rules of temple consecration every ritual had to be perfect, "otherwise people and chiefs continued indefinitely under tabu and were not allowed to come to their women folk." Because of Kahiki'ula, the set of rituals had to begin all over again, and until the temple was properly consecrated, services at all other temples and all activities requiring religious sanction had to cease (Malo 1951:160–63).

20. *Ka'a'awa* "Land section, village, elementary school, point, and stream, Waikāne and Kahana qds., O'ahu. *Lit.,* the wrasse fish" (PN). The *ahupua'a* between Kahana and Kualoa (SO map of Ko'olauloa). Located about 10 miles from Kailua.

27 So they once again traveled on until they arrived at Kaluanui.[21] The people of that place helped to build a house for them. And when their house problems had been solved, Kahiki'ula folks brought all the things required for them to live as a family.

28 Hina became pregnant with their first child. When it was born, it was a boy, and his name was called Kahikihonuakele.[22]

29 Right after that, Hina became pregnant again, and another son was born. He was called Kekelei'aikū.[23] Hina became pregnant again, and the third of the children, a baby pig, was born. This is the one whose story we are reading. The fourth of the children was born, a daughter, that is Leialoha.[24]

21. *Kaluanui* "Land section and stream, northeast Oʻahu. . . . *Lit.,* the big pit" (PN). Also the birthplace of Kamapuaʻa; an *ahupuaʻa* between Hauʻula and Punaluʻu (SO map of Koʻolauloa). Located about 15 miles from Kailua.

22. *Kahikihonuakele* *Lit.,* Tahiti-the-land-that-sails. In another version of the story alluded to by Kamakau, Hina and ʻOlopana were the parents of this child, and he was given this name because ʻOlopana and Hina's parents were from Kahiki (*Kūʻokoʻa,* January 12, 1867).

23. *Kekeleiʻaikū* Here the second-born, but foremost, guardian of Kamapuaʻa. Kamakau relates that he is the first-born of Kahiki-ʻula and Hina, his name being Kelekeleiʻaikū (*Kūʻokoʻa,* January 12, 1867). Kelekele (another form of Kekele) is "the fat part of a hog" (LAD). *ʻAikū* is "to take food that is set apart as temporarily or permanently sacred or forbidden to use. . . . To eat contrary to custom, prescribed rule, or established precedent; to overlook, disregard, or take no notice of a tabu" (AP). Hence, the literal meaning is pig-fat-that-is-eaten-irreligiously. A form of *ʻaikū, hoʻaikū* appears in Pele chants later in this version (Issue 16), and Emerson states that *hoʻaikū* are "all the male and female relatives of Hiʻiaka" (1915:53). *ʻAikū* may connote a group of people who worshiped a different set of *Akua,* other than the Kū *Akua* of the *luakini* rituals and *ʻAikapu* religion. Kekeleiʻaikū was also the name of a temple at Kawailele, ʻEwa, said to have contained the drum Kahapuʻulono or Kapaikaualulu (For. Col. 6:300). This may be a temple formerly located at Puʻukapolei (SO 53).

24. *Leialoha* In this version, she is the *kupua* sister of Kamapuaʻa. She was born as a human but

30 When this girl grew big, she flew up into the sky, and her body became a kind of rain called Kauanaulu.[25]

31 And we shall see later on in our story how this sister of Kamapuaʻa obeyed and aided him.

32 At this point, we shall forget the rain-bodied sister of Kamapuaʻa, until such time when the strength of this peculiar daughter of Hina and Kahikiʻula will be called upon.

33 Kamaunuaniho lived with her children and grandchildren. The human grandchildren, that is Kahikihonuakele and Kekeleiʻaikū, grew big during this time.

34 Kahikihonuakele adopted and raised[26] a dog, and Kekeleiʻaikū adopted a pig.[27] This pig was not just any pig, it was their younger brother who had been born as a pig.

35 Kamaunuaniho composed a name chant for her pig grandchild, and this is it below:

> *Hānau aʻe nō*
> Born indeed
>
> *ʻŌili ana i ka hau anu o ka mauna*
> Appearing in the cold dew of the mountain
>
> *ʻO Hiwahiwa ʻoe*
> You are Hiwahiwa[28]
>
> *ʻO Hamohamo*
> O Hamohamo[29]
>
> *ʻO ka maka o ka ʻōpua*
> (5) The center of the billowy cloud
>
> *I hānau ʻia i ka uka o Kaliuwaʻa*
> Born in the uplands of Kaliuwaʻa[30]
>
> *ʻO kou inoa ʻia, e ō mai*
> This is your name chant—answer!

36 And so emerged this little pig's many body forms[31] [from the power of his grandmother's chant].

sometimes becomes a rain cloud and aids Kamapuaʻa in his fight with Pele. *Lit.,* wreath of love. Seems to be an obscure figure and is not cited in Beckwith's *Hawaiian Mythology.*

25. *Kauanaulu Lit.,* the *naulu* rain. *Naulu,* "sudden shower" (PED).

26. The term is *hānai,* to feed or to raise, but also means to adopt and signifies a very close and loving relationship.

27. There is interesting symbolism here, as one brother chooses a dog as his *hānai,* while the other chooses a pig, that is, Kamapuaʻa. Later in this story, as well as in the other versions, Kamapuaʻa has a fierce battle with Kūʻilioloa, a dog *kupua* who was wont to devour humans. Kamapuaʻa, of course, was victorious.

28. *Hiwahiwa* "To be greatly loved. . . . To be pleased with; to be satisfied with, as an *Akua* with an offering. . . . To pet; to treat a child, a servant or an animal with delicacy" (LAD).

29. *Hamohamo Lit.,* anointed one.

30. *Kaliuwaʻa Lit.,* the canoe leak. The name of a valley and waterfall (known today as Sacred Falls) upland from the area known as Kaluanui, Hauʻula, Koʻolauloa, Oʻahu (PN).

31. *kinolau* "Many forms taken by a supernatural body" (PED). In the case of Kamapuaʻa, this included human, pig, *humuhumunukunuku-ā-puaʻa* (a fish), and *kūkaepuaʻa* (a plant) (Beckwith 1970:202). His plant forms also included *kukui, ʻuhaloa,* and *ʻamaʻu.*

37 The relatives of Kahikiʻula and their human children existed by climbing the mountain to snare birds.[32] The name of this mountain was Kahinahina,[33] which is a place upland of Kaliuwaʻa.

38 Their youthful days passed in this manner of the ancient times, and when they two caught their birds, they would return to the seaside, to their parents and grandmother, and also to their animals. Indeed, the days of their hungering for flesh [fish or meat] passed by at this time.

39 Kahikihonuakele also raised, besides his dog, a certain bird, and so did Kekeleiʻaikū. These cheeping birds[34] were given for his dear younger pig-brother.

40 And so their life continued until the time when these children went to farm in the uplands of Kaliuwaʻa. Kahikihonuakele prepared his bundle of taro tops[35] for the upland climb, where he would plant taro. And Kekeleiʻaikū too prepared his bundle of taro tops.

41 Their little animals also followed behind them when they climbed upland to farm.

42 Kahikihonuakele started to climb with his bundle of taro tops on his back, and Kekelei-ʻaikū followed behind with his little pig.

43 Their grandmother said, "Let's make your bundle of taro tops secure. Then we'll send it up upon your little pig so that you won't be tired.

44 "Because what else is the value of feeding little pigs? Perhaps his value is in putting your burdens upon him."

45 Kekeleiʻaikū said, "No, I will carry our burden of taro tops upon my back. I pity my little pig."

46 Kamaunuaniho knew that her pig grandchild could carry that big bundle of taro tops on his little body.

32. Bird snaring is a sign of poverty, because it requires so much effort and the resulting flesh is so little. Usually done by boys too young to fish. See also Nakuina (n.d.):6–9.

33. *Kahinahina* Here it is said to be a mountain at Kaliuwaʻa, but it is not found in PN, PSIC, or on Bier's 1976 map. Perhaps a lost place name.

34. *ʻio manu* Cheeping birds are a veiled reference to ʻOlopana's sons ʻIomea and ʻIouli, the cousins of Kamapuaʻa, who will inherit their father's position after his defeat by Kamapuaʻa. See Issue 6.

35. *huli* Taro tops refer to the way taro is planted. The top portion of the taro corm and the bottom 8 to 12 inches of the stem, called *huli*, are used for replanting a field of taro.

47 Kamaunuaniho didn't listen to what Kekelei-
'aikū was saying, but instead tied the bundles
of taro tops together securely, loaded them
upon this pig, and tied them firmly onto
both sides of the pig.

48 In no time at all Kekelei'aikū had climbed up
with his little pig brother, and they began their
farming.

49 Then Kekelei'aikū began to go and watch his
elder brother planting taro, in order to help
him, but his eldest brother said,

50 "I mistakenly thought that you were planting
your bundle of taro tops. Here you are coming
to watch me plant taro."

51 Kekelei'aikū answered, "Perhaps we two
should work together in your planting until
it's finished, and then plant all of mine. Then
two of us can return to the house together."[36]

It is not finished.

36. Kekelei'aikū's proposal reflects the concept of *laulima,* many hands working together to make heavy work light, and planting taro is exceedingly hard work. As the younger brother, his duty was to aid his elder brother. Kahiki-honuakele's rejection of this kind offer reveals the friction between the two brothers.

KAMAPUA'A

AND HIS BROTHERS

BECOME FARMERS

ISSUE 3

1   The elder brother, Kahikihonuakele, rejected the idea of his younger brother, Kekeleiʻaikū. So he returned to his own plantation.

2   Upon his return, his younger pig-brother was rooting[1] in their garden, and half of their bunch of taro tops had already been planted. Kekelei-ʻaikū was very happy that his work had been shortened.

3   Just after lunch they finished planting their bundle of taro tops. Then he said to his younger pig-brother,

4   "Let us two return first, and afterward our elder brother will return; our farming was finished through your great strength in planting. Therefore we live through you, and our parents and our grandmother live through you also."

5   In that way his elder brother praised him lovingly, while stroking his back gently with his hands.

6   Then the two of them turned toward home, and when they arrived, the parents asked,

7   "Where then is your elder brother?"

8   Kekeleiʻaikū said, "I have finished planting all my taro tops, so why should I just sit around up there?

9   "Indeed, I have returned, but I had said when we first arrived at our two plantations that we should work together in his planting, then he could help me in mine, but he refused my request. That is why he works alone in his garden."[2]

10   The parents said, "This is an amazing thing, to our way of thinking. You have already finished all of your garden, while your elder brother, who is the stronger of you two, has not."

11   "Perhaps you folks don't believe what I am saying. When Kahikihonuakele returns, then he can tell you the truth," said Kekeleiʻaikū.

1. ʻeku "To root, as a pig. Fig., prow of a canoe" (PED). Kamapuaʻa was famous for his prowess in rooting, and as it was his foremost characteristic, it is introduced early in the story. Of course, the double meaning of ʻeku is to make love, the pig's snout being a phallic symbol, and the taro garden, or loʻi, is symbolic of female genitalia from which all life, here symbolized by the taro plant, emerges. The image of pigs rooting in the loʻi usually elicits laughter from older Hawaiians.

2. It would have been expected that Kekeleiʻaikū would have stayed to help his elder brother with his work until the task was completed, as that was a younger brother's duty in former times.

12   While they were talking, Kahikihonuakele
      arrived with his little dog.

13   And Hina called to this child of theirs,

14   "Hurry up and come here. Your younger
      brother has returned first. He said that his
      garden has all been planted with taro tops.

15   "We couldn't verify that what he said was
      the truth, so we have been waiting. You are
      the one to tell us the truth."

16   "Yes, it's the truth, because when I returned
      by there I saw that his whole garden had been
      planted from one end to the other, as if some
      people had come to help him. As for my
      garden, it is not yet finished.[3] Perhaps after
      several more days of planting, mine will be
      completely finished."

17   Kamaunuaniho laughed a little because she
      knew why Kekelei'aikū had finished planting
      his garden so quickly. It was because of the
      help of his little pig-brother.

18   When the evening came, they ate a large meal,
      and when they were finished, they all returned
      outside to rest for the night.

19   The next morning, Kahikihonuakele prepared
      to go up again to finish planting his bundle of
      taro tops. Kahiki'ula said to Kekelei'aikū that
      he should go along to plant the taro tops, to
      help finish the garden of his elder brother.

20   Kekelei'aikū replied, "It would be better for my
      elder brother to stay by the sea to fish for us,
      and of the two of us, I will be the one to go
      up to finish planting his bundle of taro tops."

21   Kahiki'ula asked Kahikihonuakele, and he
      quickly agreed, because he knew that it was very
      tiring work for one man to do, as he had done
      the day before.

3. The actual term is *lawalu,*
to broil meat or fish on coals;
probably a misprint of *lawa,*
to have enough.

22   So the family sat down to eat breakfast, and when they were finished, Kekeleiʻaikū fed his little pig-brother until he was satisfied. Then they two began to climb up to the place where they were to work.

23   When they arrived there, Kekeleiʻaikū said to this little pig of his, "Here is our work, we two shall plant together the taro tops of our elder brother, because this is something eaten by all of us when the taro is mature."

24   This little pig of his began to dig, and the hands of Kekeleiʻaikū seized the cuttings, thinking he would plant them, when this little pig ran up and thrust upward at Kekeleiʻaikū's hands.

25   Then he asked this pig of his, "Don't you want us to work together?"

26   This little pig grunted. Therefore, Kekeleiʻaikū returned to the side that was shaded by some trees and made himself comfortable until he was overcome with sleep. He was suddenly awakened by the rooting of this little pig beside him.

27   He asked, "Is the work finished?" This little pig grunted.

28   When he looked carefully at the pig's work, he saw that all the taro tops had been planted from one edge of the garden to the other.

29   So the two of them turned toward their home by the sea at Kaluanui.

30   They arrived just as their elder brother Kahiki-honuakele had returned from fishing and was broiling fish on the fire. Therefore they all sat down and ate. Then the parents asked Kekeleiʻaikū,

31   "How is the garden of your elder brother?"

32   "Well, what do you think? Indeed, it has all been planted with taro cuttings. There is just one thing perhaps that we must wait for and that is the growing of the weeds. That is the time to dig up[4] the grass of our two gardens. And when the time comes to mulch the taro above with the small grass [or ferns], then nothing need be said about it—the eyes will see the food."

33   The words of Kekelei'aikū made his elder brother happy, and in that way did the parents of these two equally receive this one lesson [that each should do the work for which they are best suited].

34   Their time passed in teasing conversation as the evening descended upon them, and soon the time came when 'Lehua took away the sun.'[5]

35   At this point in our story, we shall begin to see the wondrous and supernatural deeds of this younger pig-brother of Kekelei'aikū.

36   The little pig began stealing the people's chickens, from Punalu'u[6] to Kaleoka'ō'io[7] at Kualoa.[8]

37   And on a certain night, he succeeded in stealing all the chickens of Ka'alaea.[9]

4. The text reads *alao*, probably a misprint of '*āla'a*, "to prod or dig with a stick, as in taro cultivation" (PED).

5. *i lawe ai o Lehua i ka lā* A poetic way of saying that the sun sets at Lehua, an island west of Ni'ihau, the "westernmost of the main island chain" (PN). *Lawe o Lehua i ka lā; lilo!* (Lehua takes away the sun; [it is] gone!) . . . In love chants, this saying means that one's sweetheart has been taken away (ON 1961).

6. *Punalu'u* "Village, beach park, and point, Kahana qd. . . . east O'ahu. *Lit.,* coral dived for" (PN). An *ahupua'a* between Kaluanui and Kahana (SO map of Ko'olauloa). The next valley south of Kaluanui.

7. *Kalaeoka'ō'io* "The boundary point between Ko'olau Poko and Ko'olau Loa" (PN). *Lit.,* the peninsula of the *ō'io* or bonefish. Four valleys south from Kaluanui. Also known as Kalaeoka'oi'o, or peninsula of the ghostly procession.

8. *Kualoa* "Land division, point, and beach park, Waikāne qd., O'ahu, an area anciently considered one of the most sacred places on the island. . . . A place of refuge was here. . . . *Lit.,* long back" (PN). The *ahupua'a* between Ka'a'awa and Hakipu'u (SO map of Ko'olaupoko).

9. *Ka'alaea* "Valley, land division, and stream, Waikāne qd., O'ahu. *Lit.,* the ocherous earth" (PN). The *ahupua'a* between Waiāhole and Waihe'e (SO map of Ko'olaupoko). Nine valleys south of Kaluanui.

38 When this one was returning, he was seen by the people, because morning had arrived while he was still at Waiāhole,[10] the land for which was said, 'Fetch the cooked unpounded taro at Waiāhole'[11] in the time of Kūali'i,[12] the king of O'ahu.

39 The people followed this little pig for a great distance to Kaluanui, where his parents and older brothers were living.

40 The people went and asked who owned that little pig, and indeed the natives of that area showed them.

41 In no time the people were standing outside the threshold of their house asking, "Is the pig that ran here yours, perhaps?

42 "Our chickens have been persistently stolen, and so have the chickens of half of Ko'olauloa[13] and half of Ko'olaupoko.[14] People are very angry at this little chicken-stealing pig."

43 "Perhaps it may be that it wasn't my little pig, for how could he have gone all the way to Ko'olaupoko? Here is my little pig inside his pen, fast asleep.

44 "Let's all go and see him in order to put an end to your mistaken thoughts.

45 "And what about the one that you haven't caught yet? Grab him and tie him up securely. Bring him here before me. If you want a reward, then I indeed will reward you with riches."

46 "That wasn't exactly our thought. The death of this pig, that's the only compensation to be paid us; we want no other reward," said a man.

47 When they went to this little pig's pen, the little pig was crouched down with a rather thin body, looking to them like a pig covered with sores.

10. *Waiāhole* "Land division, camp, ditch, tunnel, forest reserve, homesteads, elementary school, stream, village, and beach park, Waikāne qd., O'ahu. *Lit.,* mature *āhole* (a fish) water" (PN). The *ahupua'a* between Waikāne and Ka'alaea (SO map of Ko'olau-poko). Eight valleys south of Kaluanui.

11. *E ki'i kalo pa'a i Waiāhole* A famous saying concerning Waiāhole, where much taro is still grown. The taro is said to be hard enough to be used for fire-wood. Also figuratively refers to a stubborn man (SO 189). Similar to *ke kalo pa'a o Waiāhole* (the hard taro of Waiāhole), a reminder not to treat others badly (ON 1735).

12. *Kūali'i* was a high-ranking chief who ruled O'ahu when Keawe ruled Hawai'i, two genera-tions before Cook's arrival in 1778. Kūali'i was born at Waiāhole (Kamakau 1961:75; SO 190).

13. *Ko'olauloa* "District, northern windward O'ahu. *Lit.,* long Ko'olau" (PN). This district encompasses all the land from Kalaeoka'ō'io to the begin-ning of Waimea Bay, which is the point called Keahuohapu'u (SO 142).

14. *Ko'olaupoko* "District, southern windward O'ahu. *Lit.,* short Ko'olau" (PN). Encompasses the area from Kaleoka'ō'io to Makapu'u Point (SO 177).

48   They were in doubt. This didn't look like the pig they had chased, because that pig had had a fine body. He had been rather big and somewhat smooth and round.

49   The people said to Kekelei'aikū, "Don't you have any other pigs?"

50   Kekelei'aikū denied it, saying, "I don't have any other pigs, only that little pig."

51   The people returned empty-handed, with their hopes disappointed.

52   The news of this chicken thief traveled on until 'Olopana, the king, heard of it. At the time he was living at Kailua,[15] at a place called Wai'auwia,[16] where the broad, flat plain of 'Ālele was spread out in clear view.[17]

53   Because 'Olopana lived at Wai'auwia, that land became famous as a chiefly land. Just as in the famous saying of that ancient time:

54   'Wai'auwia separates out the child.'[18] The meaning of this saying is that a royal child belongs to this land.

55   The people went before King 'Olopana, and told him of this new event, of all the chickens being stolen by a certain pig.

56   "Therefore, O King, you should order your servants to guard your chicken roost with great care, O King, lest they be easily stolen by the pig, just as ours have been.

57   "Therefore we have come before you, to tell this news to the king."

58   At that time the servants of the king were posted to guard the chicken roost of the king, lest they be stolen like the chickens of those people that he had just heard from.

It is not finished.

15. *Kailua* "Land division, schools, bay, beach park, field, ditch, and stream, Mōkapu qd., O'ahu. *Lit.*, two seas" (PN). Formerly, many chiefs lived there because of the abundance of fish and taro. Fourteen valleys from Kaluanui.

16. *Wai'auwia* Also Wai'auia, "land area, Kailua, O'ahu. *Lit.*, water diverted" (PN). It was said that anyone coming from Wai'auia was a chief (SO 230). Near the bridge across Kawainui stream, Kailua Road (PSIC).

17. *'Ālele* "Land area in the approximate center of Kailua, O'ahu, formerly a plain called Kula-o-'Ālele, a sports area" (PN). "On this broad plain stands the Kailua theatre, the market, a service station, and the coconut grove" (SO 229).

18. *E ho'oka'awale a'e no Wai'auwia ke keiki* A witty saying, as *ka'awale* means to separate and *'auwia* to turn aside. See note 16. Not found in ON.

KAMAPUA'A STEALS

'OLOPANA'S CHICKENS

ISSUE 4

1   Who indeed was this chicken-stealing pig, who might dare to steal the king's chickens? Perhaps he wouldn't get even one little chick from the king's roosts. 'Soon the thief's little bones would be broken.'[1]

2   The little pig rested until three nights had gone by. Then this little pig began to venture forth and steal chickens again.

3   When the little pig went out on this last night, he went all the way to Kāneʻohe.[2] He persisted in stealing all the chickens of these ahupuaʻa[3] until there were none left.

4   On this morning, while he was returning, this one heard the crowing of a certain chicken. He thought that he would attack it and eat it up. So this one ran, following it upland and seaward, as that is where the chicken flew.

5   And because of these things that the chicken did, Kamapuaʻa began to think to himself that perhaps indeed this was a chicken kupua[4] that he had been chasing after.

6   Yes, O readers, this was really a chicken that could change itself magically, very much the way that Kamapuaʻa would change his strange body forms. The name of this chicken was Hoʻokahikaniakamoa,[5] who was from Kahiki.

7   As for Kaʻuhalemoa,[6] he was his younger brother. This was the chicken of the uplands of Pālolo,[7] to whom, it is said, belongs the Lililehua rain.[8]

8   So Kamapuaʻa returned to his home in Kaluanui. He just kept up this behavior until he tired himself out in chasing chickens.

9   Kekeleiʻaikū grabbed the chickens caught by Kamapuaʻa, and the elder brothers began to steam chickens as meat for their breakfast.

The original publication date for this issue (June 24) is incorrect; it was the issue for Thursday, June 25, 1891.

1. *Pau ʻē nā wahi iwi ona i ka hakihaki* As *iwi* is synonymous with life, this is a threat of death. Not found in ON.

2. *Kāneʻohe* "Quadrangle, land section . . . village, bay, beach park, harbor . . . Oʻahu. Lit., bamboo husband" (PN). The *ahupuaʻa* between Heʻeʻia and Kailua (SO map of Koʻolaupoko). Formerly known for its many taro patches and high state of cultivation (Handy and Handy 1972:455–56). Thirteen valleys south of Kaluanui.

3. *ahupuaʻa* "Land division, usually extending from the uplands to the sea" (PN). Often takes on the boundaries of the ridges that define pie-shaped valleys, typical of high islands.

4. chicken *kupua* Another example of a supernatural creature who could take many body forms at will, as did Kamapuaʻa, but in this case it was most frequently a chicken.

5. *Hoʻokahikaniakamoa* Lit., one cry of the cock. Not listed in Beckwith's *Hawaiian Mythology* and seems to be an unknown figure.

6. *Kaʻuhalemoa* Lit., my chicken house. This looks very much like Kaʻauhelumoa, a famous chicken *kupua* of Palolo. After a fight with Kamapuaʻa, Kaʻauhelumoa fell into a spring and drowned. The spring still carries this name today (SO 277).

7. *Pālolo* "Homesteads, stream, valley, . . . Honolulu. Lit., clay" (PN).

8. *Ua Lililehua* Said to have been a female lizard *kupua* who was killed by Hiʻiaka and became a kind of rain (SO 278).

10 It hadn't yet cooked when some people arrived from Kāneʻohe, traveling all the way until they reached Kaluanui. They thought that this one indeed was the pig who was eating their *kapu* chickens.

11 Shortly before this, the elder brothers of Kamapuaʻa had quickly hidden the chickens, lest they be justly caught by the people from whom the little pig had stolen them. That could easily have been the time when 'the bones of the mischievous one would be all broken.'[9]

12 These people arrived promptly at Kekeleiʻaikū's place. The natives of that place welcomed them with much affection, and the visitors all returned their affectionate greetings.

13 Right after that, these people asked, "Where is the pig who has just stolen our chickens? He ran straight to you here and he is the one we have been trailing.

14 "You must tell us honestly, and if you are hiding him, then you are the ones we will take before the king, and it is he who will soon kill you and not leave even one alive to tell the news, because the king and the commoners have been made very angry by the stealing of all their chickens by your pig."

15 Kekeleiʻaikū said, "A certain group of people have been chasing a certain pig, and they thought that it was my pig. A lot of them came to look at this little pig of mine, and all of them denied that it was he. He was not the pig that they had been chasing from Koʻolaupoko.

16 "And we all should go and look at my little pig in order to put an end to your mistaken thoughts. And when you folks have taken a good look at that little pig, then it's up to you to decide, and you may do with him as you please."

9. *ʻe hakihaki ai nā iwi o ke kolohe* This saying refers back to note 1 of this issue. Similar to *haʻihaʻi nā iwi o ke kolohe* (broken are the bones of the mischief-maker); said of one who is caught in mischief and given a trouncing (ON 410).

17 When they arrived at the pen of this little pig, he was all hunched over.

18 "And here is my little pig," said Kekeleiʻaikū.

19 The people who had chased him said, "This is not the pig. This pig is covered with sores, sleeping all hunched over. Don't you have another pig, you who live here [kamaʻāina]?"[10]

20 "Some of us will go and search[11] again. Maybe there is a big pig; then the error will be put to an end."

21 At this time some of them went out to search, while this magical little pig made himself very limp and weak. Thereafter, the people left, and they returned to Kāneʻohe with disappointed hopes.

22 And in this manner Kahikiʻula folks lived with their children. However, Kamapuaʻa did not give up his thoughts of chicken stealing.

23 Soon after a few nights had passed following the pig's escape, he again began to go out and steal chickens. This time the little pig went all the way until he reached Kailua, the place where ʻOlopana, the king, was living. The chicken caretakers of ʻOlopana watched very alertly, day and night, for the arrival of the chicken thief.

24 However, on the night when they thought no one was coming, well, that was just when this little Kamapuaʻa arrived.

25 On this night when Kamapuaʻa arrived, ʻOlopana's guards were fast asleep. The pig was quick and routed two chicken roosts, and turned to go without being seen.

26 When day came, the chicken caretakers saw that all the chickens from two chicken roosts were gone. The bodies had been consumed and only the heads remained.

10. *kamaʻāina* "Native-born, one born in a place" (PED). Often used, as in this instance, as a term of address.

11. The term used is *hoʻāla,* which actually means "to rise up, get up, come forward" (PED).

27   Therefore, the king commanded his people who raised chickens, "Sit and watch very carefully, lest all my chicken roosts soon be raided by this very great troublemaker.

28   "This lazy good-for-nothing may perhaps continue to think of his desire and that my chicken roosts would be just the thing to satisfy him on his hungry days.

29   "I am so vexed that if perhaps this thief is caught, he will soon be torn to little bits by me. Indeed, because of him I will not be eating my own chickens! Another will eat the things that I have so laboriously raised!

30   "Therefore, you folks had better keep a very careful watch from now on, and if my chicken roosts are raided again without your seeing who the thief is, then each of you shall die.

31   "And if you should actually see the thief who has raided my chicken roosts, then indeed you will live. This is my command. Return to your places to fulfill it."

32   Just after this raid upon the king's chicken roosts, Kamapua'a stayed away from them. But after five nights had passed, he began again to go after the remaining chickens of the king.

33   While he was eating the chickens, a few other chickens began to cackle. Then the guards were alerted, and they saw this pig eating up the chickens.

34   Then some of them ran to grab this little pig, and some others ran to the king and reported to him with these words:

35   "O King, the one who steals your *kapu* chickens has been caught. A pig is here! Most of us ran to seize this little chicken-stealing pig."

36   "Run quickly and seize that little pig. Tie him up and bring him here before me."

37 So these other people returned to chasing the little pig.

38 When they arrived, the others were still chasing the pig, so they went along, too. The little pig was in front, the people were behind, shouting like this:

39 "Here is the one who has been stealing the *kapu* chickens of 'Olopana the king—a pig!"

40 Because of the loud shouting of these people, all the people from Kailua to Punalu'u were also aroused.

41 The roads were full of people, and the pig was running in front while the people were chasing him behind. They all reached the river of Kahana.[12]

42 The pig quickened his pace. The people chased him all the way to the houses of Kahiki'ula folks.

It is not finished.

12. *Kahana* "Land section, quadrangle, village, valley, State park, bay, beach park, and stream, Kahana and Waikāne qds., O'ahu" (PN). The *'ahupua'a* between Punalu'u and Ka'a'awa (SO map of Ko'olauloa). Two valleys south of Kaluanui.

‘OLOPANA MAKES WAR

UPON KAMAPUA‘A

ISSUE 5

1   This little pig was found sleeping in his pen, and the name of that pen was 'Olelepā.[1] The nose of this little pig was pierced with coconut sennit, and the name of this land in Koʻolauloa was called from that very ancient time until this day Haleʻaha,[2] because of the piercing of the nose of Kamapuaʻa with coconut sennit ['aha].

2   Because of the people's very great anger, they carried him with rough hands, striking his body with clubs until blood flowed.

3   The name of this land in Koʻolau[3] was called Pāpaʻakoko,[4] for the blood of this pig who was beaten. Afterward, O reader, we shall see the deeds of this little pig.

4   Kekeleiʻaikū cried out to his little pig. The people had firmly tied this little pig and carried ['auamo][5] him off all the way to Kailua, where King 'Olopana was living, waiting for the arrival of the people with the evildoer that they had caught. This was indeed the time when his words would be fulfilled, that is to say, he would break all the bones of this mischief-maker when he saw him.

5   While the people passed by with their wrong-doer, Kekeleiʻaikū chanted plaintively[6] to his younger brother, a companion cherished by him in the 'windy rainy days of Koʻolau.'[7]

6   This perhaps is the way this little song went:

> *Kai kua Koʻolau*
> Rustic Koʻolau
>
> *Kai ʻoʻolokū ma ka makani*
> The sea is made stormy by the wind
>
> *He Kalahua na ka Hoʻoilo.*
> A Kalahua[8] rain of winter.[9]

7   Kekeleiʻaikū chanted yearningly for his pig-brother, who was being taken by the people before the king to be put to death.

1. *'Olelepā* Same as *lelepā*, "one who jumps over a fence; to fence-jump. *Fig.*, non-conformer; one who cannot be restrained, especially regarding the opposite sex" (PED).

2. *Haleʻaha* Land section and present site of Queen Liliʻuokalani Children's Center in Punaluʻu, Koʻolauloa, Oʻahu. *Lit.*, house of assembly or house of sennit.

3. *Koʻolau* The windward side of Oʻahu from Pūpūkea on the north to Makapuʻu on the south (SO map of Koʻolauloa, map of Koʻolaupoko).

4. *Pāpaʻakoko Lit.*, dried blood. The name of a land area between Kaluanui and Punaluʻu, Oʻahu (SO map of Koʻolauloa). Located at 21.38 North, 157.56 West; the southern section of two *ahupuaʻa*, the other called Papaʻanui (PSIC).

5. *'auamo* "Pole or stick used for carrying burdens across the shoulders; . . . to carry on the *'auamo. Lit.*, carrying handle" (PED).

6. *uwē helu* "A wailing call of grief and love, recounting deeds of a loved one and shared experiences; to weep and speak thus. *Lit.*, enumerating weeping" (PED).

7. *i ka lā ua, makani o ua Koʻolau la* The Koʻolau area of Oʻahu, where Kekeleiʻaikū and Kamapuaʻa were raised, is famous for its rainy, stormy beauty. While this saying figuratively signifies hardship and trouble, it also recalls the incomparable scenery of stormy Koʻolau. Because they had encountered these experiences together, they were doubly close. Not found in ON.

8. *kalahua* "Removal of taboo on fruits of land and sea, as during *makahiki* harvest ceremonies" (PED).

9. *"Kai kua Koʻolau"* This chant by Kekeleiʻaikū addresses the people of Koʻolau, whom he

8   And here below is what your author remembers as the plaintive chant of the children of Koʻolau:

9   *Kuʻu hoa i Kaualanipōlua,*[10]
     My companion in the dark pouring rain,

     Me he pō ʻokoʻa ala nō, ke aumoe o Koʻolau,
     Completely like the night, the midnight
        of Koʻolau,

     Kuʻu hoa i malu lau kī lau kukui
     My companion in the shade of the
        tī leaves,[11] the *kukui*[12] leaves,

     O Kahoʻiwai—e,
     Of Kahoʻiwai[13]

     E aloha wale.
     Only love to you.[14]

10   Kamaunuaniho said to her grandchild, "Don't cry. It is best now to end your tears for him for whom you cry, my grandchild.

11   "Your pig won't die, because he has many body forms. You just wait and watch for your pig to arrive," said his grandmother.

12   The people carried this pig to Kailua. He was carried all the way to the temple. There he would be killed, as Kuikui, the priest, had suggested to the king, ʻOlopana. This desire was to be fulfilled by the people when they finally arrived with this pig who was to be put to death.

13   Kamaunuaniho had already recalled the love for this pig-grandchild of hers. She called out the name chant of this pig.

calls "rustic" and who have captured Kamapuaʻa. The stormy sea signifies his troubled emotions. The mention of the *kalahua* rains is a subtle plea for forgiveness, playing on the word *kala,* to forgive. Not found in ON.

10. *"Kuʻu hoa i Kaualanipōlua"* This is said to be a chant for Princess Bernice Pauahi Bishop (PED 178).

11. *tī leaf* The common name for *kī, Cordyline terminalis.* Tī leaf is used by Hawaiians as a symbolic protection from evil; one wears it when going into a dangerous situation, as out to sea or up into the mountains. It is often used in religious ceremonies. The word *malu,* or shade, also implies divine protection.

12. *kukui* "Candlenut tree (*Aleurites moluccana*)" (PED). Considered a body form of Kamapuaʻa. The wood was carved in the shape of a pig's head and placed on the altar of Lono (Handy and Handy 1972:229). The *kukui* tree is also a symbol of peace, protection, and enlightenment.

13. *Kahoʻiwai* The name of a place back in the valley of Mānoa just before Lyon Arboretum (Ii 1959: 92).

14. Although this chant is said to be for Bernice Pauahi, it is used here by Kekeleiʻaikū for Kamapuaʻa. The chant speaks of the symbolic protection given by Kamapuaʻa to his elder brother. Kamapuaʻa was the *haku,* or lord; Kekeleiʻaikū was the protected servant.

14 Therefore, at this point you, the reader, shall know the grunt of this pig:

15 *A ua ʻike la—e,*
It is seen there

A ua ʻike
It is known

Ua ʻike kā wau
Indeed, I know

Nau i ʻai mai nei ke kapu moa a ʻOlopana
You were the one who ate the sacred
   chicken of ʻOlopana

ʻO ka puaʻa nui a Hina
(5) O the great pig of Hina

A ʻo ka Hiwa nui alo ʻeleʻele
O the great dark one, black-faced

A ʻo Kananakea
O the pale thin one

A ʻo Kahaheikea
O the white pig, with a spotted shoulder

A ʻo Kealoalokea
O the fair beloved one

A ʻo Kaʻehu Kalanuhe
(10) O the *kalanuhe*[15] reddish one

A ʻo Kaʻehu Kalawela
O the *kalawela*[16] reddish one

A ʻo ke ā iki, a ʻo ke ā nui
O the small jaw, O the large jaw[17]

A ʻo ke ā poko
O the short jaw

A ʻo ke ā kāhalahala
O the guilty[18] jaw

A ʻo Kamalelekū
(15) O Kama who leaps defiantly

A ʻo Kaihona
O the one who descends[19]

15. **kalanuhe** This seems to be an obscure term, not found in LAD, AP, or PED. May be similar to *Kalawela* (in note 16), which is a black caterpillar, as *nuhe* is a variant form of *ʻenuhe*, caterpillar (PED).

16. **kalawela** "A black caterpillar with a red dot at the base of the head, probably the sweet potato sphinx moth (*Herse cingulata*). It is destructive, especially of sweet potato leaves" (PED). May have been another body form of Kamapuaʻa, who also ate sweet potato leaves.

17. **ā** "Jaw, cheekbone. *Fig.*, to talk a lot, jabber. *Ke ā nui, ke ā iki*, big jaw, little jaw (bragging and wheedling, as of a man seeking the favor of a woman)" (PED).

18. **kāhalahala** "*He kāhalahala, ua palai*" (LAD), meaning *kāhalahala*, is like *palai*, "to be ashamed and turn the face away, as one who is conscious of guilt" (LAD).

19. **ihona** Lit., "descent, incline" (PED). Used as an epithet for Kamapuaʻa, but is in a strange grammatical position.

A ʻo i hele ma ke ʻekuna
Rooting[20] as he wanders

A ʻo Haunuʻu, a ʻo Haulani
O proud one, O rooting one

A ʻo Haʻalokuloku
O pouring rain[21]

A ʻo ka manō ka iʻa nui
(20)   O shark, the great fish

A ʻo Uʻi, a ʻO Uilani
O handsome youth, O restless one

Ko inoa puaʻa ia, e ō mai.
Here is your pig name chant—answer!

16   This pig grunted and also wriggled, and that was when the coconut sennit rope that had bound him was broken in two. He then began to eat all the people except for Kāehukū.[22] Indeed, Kamapuaʻa saved him so that he might have one left to tell the king the frightening news of what he had done.

17   Then this pig started peacefully back to Kaluanui, their family home.

18   Again ʻOlopana commanded Kāehukū to call out the people of Waimānalo,[23] seeking them also at Kona,[24] continuing to Waiʻanae,[25] to join together to once again fetch the pig at Kaluanui, and to beat him to death.

19   When the people had assembled, they began their procession to Kaluanui.

20   All of the family of Kamaunuaniho gathered together to ascend to the uplands of Kaluanui. The people went up by way of 'the big canoe of Kaliuwaʻa.'[26] The face of the pig was turned upward, and the people climbed up on the nipples of the pig, lest they be captured by the king. Therefore, 'the *akule* fish had already fled to the deep waters.'[27]

20. **ʻekuna** This term is not found in LAD or PED but seems to be a form of *ʻeku*, "to root, as a pig" (PED).

21. **Haʻalokuloku** "To pour, as rain . . . to be agitated" (PED). Used in describing Kamapuaʻa in his name chant. See Issue 1, note 4.

22. **Kāehukū** Lit., the tossed spray, *kāehu* being a form of *kaiehu* (PED). In other versions, Kamapuaʻa spares Makaliʻi to tell the news (For. Col. 5:342; Kahiolo 1978:22–26).

23. **Waimānalo** Lit., potable water. An *ʻahupuaʻa* between Kailua and Makapuʻu Point. (SO map of Koʻolaupoko). Formerly belonged to one of the Māui brothers, Māuimua (*Kūʻokoʻa*, November 27, 1875). Fifteen valleys south of Kaluanui.

24. **Kona** Lit., south. Usually refers to the southern sectons of islands. This Kona is the name of the district from Maunalua to Moanalua, Oʻahu. In 1859 the name was changed to Honolulu, and the above are the present boundaries of the district of Honolulu (SO 257).

25. **Waiʻanae** Lit., mullet water. The name of a district on Oʻahu, stretching from Nānākuli to Kaʻena point (SO 80).

26. **ka waʻa nui o Kaliuwaʻa** Refers to an upright section of the cliff, just to the left of the falls, which looks like a canoe hull. Not found in ON.

27. **āhaʻi ʻē no ke akule i ka hohonu** The *akule* fish is *Trachurops crumenophthalmus*. Fig., the prey has escaped. A similar saying is "*ua wehe ke akule i ka hohonu*, the *akule* has fled to the depths [of escape]" (PED, *akule*). Not found in ON. Refers to the escape of the family of Kamapuaʻa.

21 The very last to ascend was their grandmother, whereupon the front of the pig was turned downward as a sign of respect, and his grandmother climbed upon his back until she stood upon the cliff.

22 And here upon the well-traveled path was the procession of the king and his great multitude of followers.

23 'Olopana and his people finally arrived at Kaluanui. The king rested on this evening to ease the pain of his stiff body, unaccustomed to such travel.

24 And when it grew light, some spies were sent to climb above Kaliuwaʻa to look for this pig.

25 The pig was at that time at 'Oilowai,[28] sleeping in the shade of a certain large rock.

26 When the men climbed up and arrived at the place where the pig was sleeping, none of them even saw this pig. But one of them saw him, namely, Kiʻei,[29] because he was on the other side of the cliff.

27 So he called out to some of the others, "Here is the pig, under the shade of the rock. Look carefully."

28 When his companions looked down carefully, they all finally saw him. So they turned to go before the king, 'Olopana.

29 Upon their arrival at the seashore, they revealed this, "There is the pig, at the edge of the cliff at 'Oilowai!"

30 The procession of the king quickly began to ascend the valley to meet with the pig.

31 "Tie the pig securely with large braided sennit ropes, so that he cannot move again.

32 "This pig might perhaps escape from a thin rope. He is the one that squirms, but this rope will not be broken by the pig."

28. *'Oilowai Lit.*, water of the *'oilo* fish. *'Oilo*, "name of a species of fish" (LAD). The name of a pool where Kamapuaʻa and his family used to bathe, at Kaliuwaʻa (*Ka Hōkū o ka Pakipika,* November 14, 1861).

29. *Kiʻei Lit.*, "to peer, peep" (PED). Here it is said to be the name of a cliff. Listed as an *Akua* of Kamapuaʻa in "*Na Wahi Pana o Kaliuwaʻa*" (*Ka Hoku o ka Pakipika,* November 14, 1861).

33 The king urged them to climb quickly, 'to hasten for the food of Hinakahua.'[30]

34 The supernatural pig body of Kamapua'a was lying down in the stream, and the water of the stream was stopped from flowing. The water had backed up into the uplands and was rising on either side of the cliff.

35 And here was the procession of people nearing the spot where this pig was sleeping.

36 As for the king, 'Olopana, he was the last one climbing up there.

37 The pig knew that the people had almost arrived at the very spot where he was pretending to sleep so mischievously.

38 Then this pig began to squirm and thus free the river.

39 That was the moment when the water flowed with its greatest strength like an extraordinary sudden rainshower, with 'double the sound of Ka'uluwena.'[31]

40 And that was the moment when the men were enveloped by the water, flowing with its great strength.

41 None of them survived to tell the news. Their corpses were left upon the land and in the ocean.

42 However, King 'Olopana did not die in this great flood. He turned to go down the road with a gut full of anger for a certain pig.

43 But his anger was in vain, because he could not be victorious over the matchless and mysterious strength of that pig.

44 Meanwhile, his warriors had fought twice, and there was a long list of mistakes that had been made by his commoners. They hadn't won in the least over the grandchild of Kamaunuaniho.

30. *E ho'olohe nō nā 'ai o Hina-kahua* "The food of Hinakahua" may signify the spoils of victory, as Hinakahua was a "former site for dancing, *maika*, the *kilu* sexual game . . . and fighting (*mokomoko*), Kapa'au, Hawai'i. *Lit.,* Hina's arena" (PN). Not found in ON.

31. *kaulua ke kani o Ka'uluwena* Ka'uluwena was a woman, also called Mapunaia'a'ala, the daughter of Kūheleipō and Haumea (Kamakau 1964:68); however, the inspiration for this saying is obscure. Not found in ON.

45 The king finally returned to his royal house in Kailua. Only the house was standing; there were no people to give it warmth and affection [as they had all been killed in battle].

46 As for the old men, the old women, and the children, they were the people who assembled at the entrance to the house of the king.

47 Therefore, the king left there and returned to dwell in Wai'anae, in order to fatten up the warriors once again.

48 Because of the many jealous thoughts held by this king for a certain pig, he thought that in the heat of their next battle, victory would be granted to him.

49 When the king saw that he had enough warriors, he sent one of his messengers to go and look for this aforementioned pig at Kaluanui.

50 Directly after all the people had been swept away in the flood, Kamapua'a and his family left Kalunui, and they returned to live in the uplands of Wai'anae, at the place called Pāhoa.[32]

51 The messengers of 'Olopana were searching for this little pig. However, he was not found in a search of the Ko'olau area. As the messengers returned by the road at Kolekole,[33] they went down toward the seashore of Wai'anae. Upon reaching Pāhoa, they all saw the little pig sleeping beneath a rock, in a space shaded from the sun.

52 So they returned and told the king about their having found the pig in the uplands of Wai'anae, sleeping under a rock.

53 When the king heard that here, close-by, was his enemy, he quickly ordered his warriors to prepare to climb up to capture the little pig.

32. *Pāhoa* Lit., dagger. A place "at the head of the Wai'anae valley wherein is situated the sugar mill of the Wai'anae Company, the shore section of which is Pokai" (SO 72). Refers to the stone dagger used to stab Kamapua'a below.

33. *Kolekole* Lit., raw, inflamed (PED). Name of the "pass and road from Schofield Barracks through the Wai'anae Range, O'ahu" (PN).

54   In the ascent by the king and his soldiers, the
     plain was filled with a great many people, from
     Waiʻanae by the sea all the way to the uplands
     of Waiʻanae.

55   When they arrived in the very early morning,
     they found this little pig still sleeping.

56   After they had seized him and bound him
     tightly, they carried him on a large carrying
     pole for the return trip to Waiʻanae. And they
     stabbed his little body with daggers, that is,
     the stone dagger.

57   His blood flowed like water, his legs as well as
     his body were cut to pieces, and the little pig
     did not wriggle at all upon the necks of the
     men who bore the carrying pole.

It is not finished.

KAMAPUA'A DEFEATS 'OLOPANA
AND VISITS KAHIKI

ISSUE 6

1   While the people were stabbing Kamapua'a with 1. See Issue 5, paragraph 15.
daggers, his elder brother Kekelei'aikū suddenly
had a premonition, and he cried out in terror.

2   Then his grandmother replied, "Sit quietly,
Grandchild, your younger brother will soon
arrive before you."

3   Then Kamaunuaniho began to call out the name
chant of this aforementioned pig-grandchild
of hers.

4   At this point, if it please the readers, there is
a short clarification below:

5   Previously recounted in the first name chant
that Kamaunuaniho had chanted[1] were the *kapu*
chickens of the king that the pig had eaten. And
to this chant one line was added: at this place
are these lines here below:

6   *A ua 'ike la—e*
It is seen there

A ua 'ike
It is known

Ua 'ike kā wau
Indeed, I know

Nau i 'ai mai nei kānaka a me ke 'Olopana,
You were the one who ate the men
    belonging to 'Olopana

'O ka pua'a nui a Hina
(5)   O the great pig of Hina

A 'o ka Hiwa nui alo 'ele'ele
O the great dark one, black-faced

A 'o Kananakea
O the pale thin one

A 'o Kahaheikea
O the white pig, with a spotted shoulder

A 'o Kealoalokea
O the fair beloved one

A ‘o Ka‘ehu Kalanuhe
(10)   O the *kalanuhe* reddish one

A ‘o Ka‘ehu Kalawela
O the *kalawela* reddish one

A ‘o ke ā iki, a ‘o ke ā nui
O the small jaw, O the large jaw

A ‘o ke ā poko
O the short jaw

A ‘o ke ā kāhalahala
O the guilty jaw

A ‘o Kamalelekū
(15)   O Kama who leaps defiantly

A ‘o Kaihona
O the one who descends

A ‘o i hele ma ke ‘ekuna
Rooting as he wanders

A ‘o Haunu‘u, a ‘o Haulani
O proud one, O rooting one

A ‘o Ha‘alokuloku
O pouring rain

A ‘o ka manō ka i‘a nui
(20)   O shark, the great fish

A ‘o U‘i, a ‘O Uilani
O handsome youth, O restless one

Ko inoa pua‘a ia, e ō mai.
Here is your pig name chant—answer!

7   Then this pig roared and also moved, and
the people shouted, "The pig lives again!"

8   *E—papapa‘u kākou e ke ali‘i i ka make*
        i ka pua‘a e—
All of us, O King, shall be killed by the pig

Nolaila, ua hū ka pua‘a e—
Therefore, the pig roars

Ke ʻeku nei ka puaʻa e—
The pig is rooting [in the earth]

Ke nū nei ka puaʻa e—
The pig is grunting

(5)
Ke keha nei ka puaʻa e—
The pig is snapping his teeth

Ke amu nei ka puaʻa e—
The pig eats voraciously

Ke ʻai mai nei ka puaʻa iā kākou e—
The pig is eating us all

Pau loa kākou i ka make e—
We are all of us finished by death.

9 There were no survivors in this eating by the pig, including King ʻOlopana and his commoners. ʻThe doors of the houses of Waiʻanae were closed with the *ʻaweoweo* fishʻ[2] during this time. These days were a pathetic, dreadful time.

10 Then the pig returned to Kekeleiʻaikū and his own people, whereupon his guardians were very happy.

11 Thereafter, they lived during these days at Pāhoa without a thought about trouble, because the king was dead.

12 Soon after these days, they returned to Kaluanui at Koʻolauloa. This land had become very beloved by Kamaunuaniho folks; that was the reason for their returning once more to Koʻolau.

13 This news of the deaths of King ʻOlopana and the commoners of Koʻolau finally reached Māui. Therefore, the children of ʻOlopana, that is to say ʻIouli[3] and ʻIomea,[4] desired to sail over and reign upon the throne of their father, who had died. And they two returned to reign as kings of Oʻahu.

2. *Ua pani ʻaweoweo ʻia ka puka o nā hale o Waiʻanae* ʻĀweoweo, "various Hawaiian species of *Priacanthus*" (PED). "Appearance of schools of this fish near shore was an omen that royalty would die" (PED, *ʻalalauwa*). Hence, *ʻaweoweo* is associated with death. Not found in ON.

3. *ʻIouli Lit.*, "a dark *ʻio*, hawk" (PED).

4. *ʻIomea Lit.*, "a variety of *ʻio* hawk without dark markings" (PED).

14 Kamapua'a left O'ahu and sailed for the Pillars of Kahiki. In this journey of his, there were many *kupua* that met with him on his path, and these were:

15 Kū'ilioloa, Keaunuileinahā, Keaumiki, Keaukā, Kalei, Ka'alemoe, Ka'alehāko'iko'i, Ka'alekualono, Kahe'enui, Kanalukuakahi through the ten waves, Kapūko'akū, Kapūko'amoe, Kapapakū, Kapapainaoa, Kapapalimukala, Kapapalimukohu, Pai'ea, 'A'ama, Hā'uke'uke, 'Opihi, Pipipi, 'Ōunauna, Ālealea, 'Ōhikimakaloa, Keonepōhuehue, 'Okapalipūkē, Makuaoka'ōlelo, Makuaokapule, Kapalimoe, Kāne, Kanaloa, Kenāmū, Kenāwā, Kahuhupāolā'au.[5]

16 They were all defeated. And Kamapua'a finally arrived at the house of the youngest daughter of Koea,[6] that is, Kaikiha'akūlou.[7] Her elder sister was Kekaiha'akūlou.[8] She was the woman who lived with Lonoka'eho.[9] The place where they lived was way up in the mountains, just below a very steep cliff.

17 No people went there; the strength of this man was such that if he became angry he would 'make the earth bitter.'[10] With his own hands he would dig, or with the attachments upon his foreheads.

18 The name of one of his foreheads was Leleinahā,[11] and the second of his foreheads was Wawakaikalani.[12]

19 When Kaikiha'akūlou saw this handsome young man, the likes of whom had not been seen in Kahiki, this girl fell down in a kind of faint.

20 When Kamapua'a saw this pretty girl fall down, he went and massaged[13] her, and when she was revived from her faint, this beauty gave her 'thanks' to the young man, and he reciprocated.

21 He passed the night there, a night and two days, and the father of this beauty was puzzled that she did not appear even at mealtime. Therefore

5. In this paragraph, all the various opponents supposedly defeated by Kamapua'a are brought together and listed. However, besides Kū'ilioloa, none of these alleged opponents were in any other Kamapua'a story. Toward the end the list becomes humorous.

Kū'ilioloa Lit., ku-the-long-dog; "a giant man-dog. He was killed by Kamapua'a" (PED). See also Beckwith 1970:347–48.

The next three are ocean currents.

Keaunuileinahā Lit., the strong current of the four jumping-off places.

Keaumiki Lit., the outgoing tide; a tide *kupua* (Beckwith 1970:354).

Keaukā Lit., the canoe-paddling tide; another tide *kupua*, who with Keaumiki was a paddler of Pele's canoe when she came from Kahiki (Beckwith 1970:169).

Kalei Lit., the wreath. Not a known mythological figure.

The next five names refer to types of waves:

Ka'alemoe Lit., the calm wave.

Ka'alehāko'iko'i Lit., the agitated wave.

Ka'alekualono Lit., the overturning wave.

Kahe'enui Lit., the large surf.

Kanalukuakahi Lit., the first wave.

The next five are types of reefs:

Kapūko'akū Lit., the emerging coral head.

Kapūko'amoe Lit., the coral head lying in ambush or the prostrated coral head.

Kapapakū Lit., the ocean floor.

Kapapainaoa Lit., the *inaoa* reef. *Inaoa* would seem to be a type of seaweed or sea creature, but is not listed in PED or LAD.

Kapapalimukala Lit., the *limukala* reef. *Limukala* are "common, long, brown seaweeds

(*Sargassum* spp.)" (PED).
Kapapalimukohu *Lit., the limu-*
kohu reef. *Limukohu* is "a soft,
succulent red seaweed (*Aspara-*
gopsis sanfordiana)" (PED).

The next eight are types of sea
creatures:
Pai'ea "An edible crab, found
where the *'a'ama* is found, but
with a harder shell and shorter
legs . . . perhaps one of the grap-
sids; . . . *fig.*, a star athlete"
(PED).
'A'ama "A large, black, edible
crab (*Grapsus grapsus tenuicrus-*
tatus) that runs over shore
rocks" (PED).
Hā'uke'uke "An edible variety
of sea urchin (*Podophora*
atrata)" (PED).
'Opihi "Limpet, any of several
species of *Helcioniscus*" (PED).
Pipipi "General name for small
mollusks, including *Nerita picea*
and *Nerita neglecta*" (PED).
'Ōunauna "Same as *unauna*,
hermit crab" (PED).
Ālealea "A shellfish (*Plectorema*
striata)" (PED).
'Ōhikimakaloa "A variety of
edible crab (no data). *Lit.*, long-
eyed *'ōhiki*" (PED).

The remaining eleven form an odd
assortment:
Keonepōhuehue *Lit.*, the sands
of the *pōhuehue* vine.
Pōhuehue "The beach morn-
ing-glory (*Ipomoea pes-caprae*),
a strong vine found on sandy
beaches in the tropics." It is
believed that if one strikes the
ocean with this vine the sea will
become rough (PED).
'Okapalipūkē *Lit.*, the beaten
cliff. An obscure term.
Makuaoka'ōlelo *Lit.*, parent of
the word.
Makuaokapule *Lit.*, parent of
the prayer.
Kapalimoe *Lit.*, the prostrate
cliff.

Kāne *Lit.*, man. One of the pri-
mordial Hawaiian *Akua*, often
said to have come to Hawai'i
from Kahiki with Kanaloa
(Kamakau 1964:67). "A god of
sunlight, fresh water and forests
. . . to whom no human sacri-
fices were made" (PED 387).
Kanaloa "One of the four great
gods. . . . His companion and
leader was Kāne. They were
renowned as kava drinkers,
and they found water in many
places. . . . Some considered
him a god of the sea" (PED).
Kenāmū *Lit.*, the *Nāmū*,
"legendary little people.
Lit., the silent ones" (PED).
Kenāwā *Lit.*, the Nāwā; "legendary little people" (PED).
Lit., the loud, babbling ones.
Kahuhupāolā'au *Lit.*, the
"borer that digs wood; . . . *fig.*,
slanderer, defamer" (PED).

6. **Koea** *Lit.*, "scratched, eroded"
(PED). Said here to be a chief
of Kahiki; in another version he
is a chief of Kaua'i (For. Col. 5:
326–33). Usually portrayed as
the father-in-law of Kamapua'a.

7. **Kaikiha'akūlou** *Lit.*, the little
one who bows her head; the first
wahine of Kamapua'a.

8. **Kekaiha'akūlou** *Lit.*, the sea
that bends down. In the Kahiolo
version, her name is Kekaiha'a-
kūloulaniokahiki (1978:30, 42, 140).

9. **Lonoka'eho** *Lit.*, Lono-the-
stone-pile. An *Akua* from Kahiki
who had eight stone foreheads
(For. Col. 5:326–33).

10. *e ho'awa ana 'o ia i ka*
honua The meaning of this saying
is obscure. Not found in ON.

11. **Leleinahā** *Lit.*, to leap into
oblivion.

12. **Wawakaikalani** *Lit.*, flash-
ing-in-the-heavens.

13. The term used is *lomi*,
"to rub, press, squeeze, crush . . .
massage . . . to work in and out"

he sent one of his servants to go and search for the royal child. Perhaps she had become sick; perhaps not.

22 When the servant arrived, the royal child was sitting, with a fine healthy body. So he returned and revealed to them that the royal daughter had found a handsome young man to live with.

23 When Koea heard of this, it became a very good thing in his opinion. "Perhaps this will be a son-in-law 'to give life to these bones,'[14] not like that son-in-law of mine who lives in the mountain. When he becomes angry with the commoners of the land, that's when he comes down and destroys everything with great terror.

24 "So tomorrow morning I shall climb up to see this new son-in-law of mine."

25 And on the next day he climbed up there to meet with his son-in-law. Upon his arrival they greeted each other affectionately, and when that was finished, a dining table was prepared laden with food, befitting that rank of the great kings of this world, simply bedecked with food.

26 They sat down to eat with great happiness, and when they were finished, Koea asked him,

27 "Where are you from?"

28 "I am from right here," answered Kamapua'a, not having decided what his name should be for them.

29 "There are no men of this place," said Koea.

30 "I have come from the sea," answered Kamapua'a.

31 "Yes, it is true that you really have come from the sea." And he was called by Koea "Kanaka-okai,"[15] because he had arrived upon the shore from the sea.

32 After only a few weeks had passed, Kamapua'a asked his *wahine,*

(PED), which recalls *lomi a ke aloha,* the squeeze of love, a phrase used in love chants as a euphemism for lovemaking.

14. *e ola ai nei mau iwi* Fig., to prolong one's life. See Issue 1, note 41; Issue 4, notes 1, 9. Similar to *ola na iwi* (the bones live); said of a respected oldster who is well cared for by his family (ON 2488).

15. *Kanakaokai Lit.,* man-of-the-sea.

33 "Are you the only one perhaps that your parents have given birth to?"

34 "There are two of us. My elder sister is there in the uplands of the mountain, where she lives with her *kāne* Lonoka'eho. He is a powerful man, skilled in fighting. His foreheads can cut trees and rocks. The people of our land here are terrified on account of him, because his strength exceeds that of all others."

35 Kamapua'a said, "Perhaps his strength is that he indeed is the only strong man of your land here.

36 "And if indeed another strong man is found, 'his feet will kick.'[16] So I shall climb up to meet with him. I want to witness his strength."

It is not finished.

16. *kaka ka wawae ona* This seems to signify defeat. Not found in ON.

KAMAPUAʻA

CHALLENGES LONOKAʻEHO

ISSUE 7

1   His *wahine* objected, "You mustn't climb into
     the uplands. Let's you and I stay here. If you
     must climb up, then let us both climb up."

2   "You stay here in this house of ours until
     I return."

3   "You won't return alive; that is the reason
     for my refusing to part with you. Let's you
     and I stay here. Don't be so stubborn."

4   "It won't be like that. You have already chosen
     death for me. Who then is the one who takes
     pleasure in this unpleasant matter of death?
     So don't you try to detain me. We two
     [Lonokaʻeho and himself] are just boys."

5   Because of his stubbornness, his *wahine* ceased
     her objections. So when 'the sun stood directly
     upon the brain,'[1] he went right up, directly
     above the cliff, to search for the plain where
     Lonokaʻeho was living with his *wahine.*

6   When Lonokaʻeho saw this man standing
     so haughtily upon the height of the cliff, he
     called out,

7   "Where have you come from, O haughty man,
     trespassing here upon my sacred mountain?
     Haven't you heard then that this upland is
     sacred to Lonokaʻeho, the strong man?"

8   "Indeed, because I have heard I climbed up
     here, because of my desire to break off those
     protruding foreheads of yours. So why don't
     you climb up here to meet with me, so that the
     boyish games of war can proceed. You perhaps
     are the native-born; I perhaps am the stranger."

9   "You are strong," said Lonokaʻeho. "That's what
     I'm thinking."

10   "What do you think, O Lonokaʻeho—are you
     really a man?"

1. *ke kūpono ʻana o ka lā i ka lolo*
A common saying referring to
high noon. *Kau ka lā i ka lolo,
hoʻi ke aka i ke kino* (the sun stands
over the brain, the shadow retreats
into the body); said of high noon,
when the sun is directly overhead
and no shadows are seen—an
important time for some ancient
rites and ceremonies (ON 1611).

11 "It's like this. All the parts of my body are only rock. The only place that's different is the genitals. And what about your strength, O Stranger?"

12 Kamapua'a said, "All of me is only rock. And as for my genital, it is 'a foundation of rock that is easily taken.'² And that is what you should hear."

13 "You really are strong," said Lonoka'eho. "'The daub of old *poi* in the calabash scatters in every direction.'³ So you should come down here so that you and I can fight."

14 "Perhaps your strength can't stand in this narrow place to fight. You climb up above here," said Kamapua'a.

15 Lonoka'eho climbed up with his two sharp foreheads and said, "It is better that you, the stranger, should be the first of the two of us to strike a blow."

16 "You, the native-born, should be first," said Kamapua'a.

17 Then Lonoka'eho grabbed the pounding forehead attached to his head, and began to cut the mountain. He thought to himself that his opponent was dead, but when his forehead returned to join with his body, Kamapua'a stood up again before him.

18 "I was thinking that you were dead," said Lonoka'eho.

19 "So that's all your strength can do! If you go down to your stronghold, then 'the life at Hilo has no canoes,'"⁴ said Kamapua'a.

20 At this time, Lonoka'eho seized the second of his foreheads. Then this forehead began to cut up the forests 'until it swam in the deep sea.'⁵ And when it was finished, it returned to join with his body. In order to look at what had been done, Lonoka'eho stood up.

2. *he papa pōhaku pānoa* The double meaning here is that his genital is like a hard rock that is easily taken by women. *Pānoa, lit.,* "to touch freely" (PED). This is a taunt to Lonoka'eho as Kamapua'a boasts of his manliness. Not found in ON.

3. *ke lele li'ili'i lā ka pala 'ai kahiko o ka 'umeke* "The daub of old poi," referring to Kamapua'a, is rather despicable, and as it "scatters in every direction," is also weak. Lonoka'eho makes this disparaging remark to weaken Kamapua'a with the power of the spoken word. Not found in ON.

4. *a'ole nō i wa'a ka noho 'ana i Hilo* Seems to be a portent of death, because canoes symbolize the human body (Emerson 1909:95), but the background of this saying is obscure. Not found in ON.

5. *a 'au i ke kai hohonu* 'The deep sea' refers to an excess of action or emotion. Not found in ON.

21 "The opponent does not die, Lonokaʻeho. You thought perhaps that you possessed enough strength. You should fight with all of your great strength lest you soon be killed by me. And if you desire your life, then apologize to me," said Kamapuaʻa.

22 "What is there for me to apologize to you about? Because, 'this is my taro and my fish.'[6] These things are my strength. It is 'a loving sweetheart to me,'"[7] said Lonokaʻeho.

23 "Perhaps your strength only appears when you fight with children and women. Now you have me, a boy, to contend with. 'Perhaps Kaʻukuʻiki[8] and his younger brothers often plead for mercy from you, and perhaps the nit often cries out to his parent, the louse,'"[9] said Kamapuaʻa.

24 No sooner had their conversation ended than Kamapuaʻa quickly picked up his spear. "Take care for your life, lest you soon be routed by the pig-grandchild of Kamaunuaniho."

25 He thrust his spear, so that fending it off was the work of Lonokaʻeho. The spear passed straight through his body, and 'he lay down in the sleep of summer and winter.'[10]

26 Then this pig of ours knew for himself that his opponent was dead. He began to climb down the precipitous cliff.

27 He went to fetch the elder sister of his *wahine*. Upon his arrival, Kamapuaʻa implored her, "Let's you and I return to the home of your parents, to live affectionately, indeed as I do with your younger sister, my *wahine*, and with the commoners."

28 Kekaihaʻakūlou agreed to this fine idea of their *kāne*'s. So she prepared herself, and when she was finished, they began their return.

6. *o kaʻu ʻai kēia me kaʻu iʻa* That is, fighting is just as natural to Lonokaʻeho as is eating fish and taro.

7. *he ipo aloha naʻu* Fighting is as enjoyable to Lonokaʻeho as is lovemaking.

8. *Kaʻukuʻiki* Lit., the little flea.

9. *e mimiha paha auaneʻi ʻo Kaʻukuʻiki pōkiʻi mā iā ʻoe, a e uwē auaneʻi, paha ka liha i kona makua he ʻuku* Fig., "perhaps lesser men beg you for mercy, as the nit does to the louse." Hence, Kama reviles Lonokaʻeho by comparing him to a bothersome louse, while those he had previously conquered were just louse eggs. Not found in ON.

10. *moe aku la i ka moe kau a hoʻoilo* This saying signifies death, as *moe* refers to defeat and/or sleep, and summer and winter represent eternity (PED, *kau* 2). *Moe i ka moe kau a hoʻoilo* (asleep with the sleep that lasts through summers and winters); death (ON 2168).

29 When these two arrived by the seashore, the parents and the chiefly relatives of their parents knew that these were 'the hours of love.'[11] Much affection was exchanged between the child and the parents, and between the younger sister and the first-born.

30 And it was that way with the commoners, too, and the royal court lived in happiness for one 'week,'[12] with a great deal of feasting everywhere in the land.

31 Her parents asked, "How did you two escape from your *kāne?*"

32 "He was killed by this one here. This one was very strong, as I myself witnessed when they fought. That is the reason for my return, and I am happy in our being reunited again as parent and child."

33 "What then shall be my reward to repay the one who has saved me? I am thinking that there is only one payment that I can give; that is, 'the bones.'[13] If it pleases him, I shall live in his presence as an attendant servant to him. Or else our kingdom, together with the commoners, should be given as just payment for my life."

34 "This is a good thing," said their parent. "We shall all live as servants under him."[14] They made this decision with one mind.[15]

35 Thereafter, they revealed to Kanakaokai what they had discussed. He replied,

36 "I will not accept your decision as binding, and furthermore, I have no desire to be rewarded in wealth for what I have done to Lonoka'eho. There is only one payment that I desire; that is love.

37 "For I am already in your debt for the boundless generosity that your two daughters have shown me in that time when I lived as a guest with all of you here. Therefore you should put an end to your idea."

11. *he mau hora ia o ke aloha* This is certainly a "newly" coined saying, as the idea of "hours" is post-European. Not found in ON.

12. The actual term used is *anahulu*, which is ten days; however, the Hawaiian "week" was reckoned as ten days, with three "weeks" equal to one lunar month.

13. *'O nā iwi* Again refers to one's life. See also Issue 1, note 39; Issue 4, notes 1, 9; and Issue 6, note 14.

14. *he kauā lawelawe* Also has the connotation of sacrificial victim, *kauā* meaning either servant or a person reserved for sacrifice to the war *Akua* Kū, when no wrongdoer was available.

15. The term used, *nā'au*, actually means "intestines, bowels" (PED), but Hawaiians believe that all emotions and thoughts are centered in the intestines. Hence, *nā'au* corresponds more accurately with "mind" in English.

38 So they just put an end to their idea and merely lived together.

39 After a few days, the chief proclaimed to his commoners that they should build a house for his daughters and their husband. He was living as the steersman for these canoes at this time.[16]

40 The commoners fulfilled the command[17] of their chief. And when it was completed, Kamapua'a and his *wāhine* went inside this house.

41 Many days passed while they three were living together, and this one began to truly enjoy this life in the village of Kahiki.

42 It was like that expression of affection [composed] for our young chiefs who have already passed away, similar to this:

> *E walea iki a'e ana*
> He was enjoying it somewhat
>
> *Me ke kai lu'a i ka 'ili*
> Like the sea that is soft upon the skin.[18]

43 In that way, Kamapua'a passed away the time while living together as one household with his wives in this foreign land.

It is not finished.

16. Canoes here figuratively refer to the two chiefesses; Kamapua'a is the steersman. This is a joke because *ho'okele,* or steersman, has sexual overtones.

17. The term is *leo,* or voice, but the voice of the chief was equal to a command, and to disobey meant death.

18. It is not known today for which chief this was written, nor the background of it. Not found in ON.

THE FIRES OF PELE

COME TO FETCH KAMAPUAʻA

ISSUE 8

1 The commanding voice of the chief Koea proclaimed to his commoners that they should build a house for his daughters and their *kāne*.

2 One *ka'au*[1] was the length of the house. The feathers of the birds of the mountain were the thatching outside. The bones of the birds were the rafters, and the hair of the people were the ropes.[2]

3 It was built in one day, thatched in one day, and furnished with everything required for the inside of the house. And their two children slept there on that very night.

4 Messengers were sent on a journey from one end of the land to the other to make the proclamation for the commoners to hear.

5 When the commoners heard this command of the chief, they said, "We thought it was the command of the chief." And the commoners fulfilled it as if it were a royal decree.

6 And on this very night, the female chiefs and their *kāne* were there inside this house where they passed the night. They lived there in comfort.

7 And then, one night the fires of Pele[3] came from Hawai'i to fetch[4] him, to entice Kamapua'a to rise and return to his beloved native sands of Hawai'i.

8 On this night, Kamapua'a awoke and squatted on his haunches. One of his *wāhine* was startled and asked him, "What are you doing awake?"

9 "I am just sitting around," replied Kamapua'a.

10 The second of the *wāhine* was suddenly awakened by the soft and sweet voices of these two, and then all three of them were awake.

11 Because Kamapua'a was upset that his *wāhine* had awakened with him, he urged that they three return to sleep.

1. *ka'au* "The number forty; applied in counting fish" (LAD). However, *ka'au* as used in the text (as a unit of measurement) is unknown today. Perhaps it came to mean forty feet.

2. These peculiar materials used in building their house indicated that the house and its occupants would be sacred, because bird feathers were *kapu* to the chiefs, bird bones used as rafters would be magical, and human hair was often used in securing the sacred whale tooth pendant. Similar to Mō'ikeha's house, named Moa-'ulanuiākea (For. Col. 4:170).

3. *Pele* "The volcano goddess born as a flame in the mouth of Haumea" (PED 396).

4. The term used is *ki'i, lit.,* "to fetch, procure . . . to seek for sexual ends" (PED). *Ki'i* is repeatedly used with sexual overtones in the text. See Issue 2, note 7.

12　As he was closing his eyes, the fire jabbed at his eyes. Therefore, this one began to chant like this:

13　*Ke kiʻi mai nei ke ahi a ke Akua wahine*
　　　o Puna iaʻu e hele—
　　The fire of the female God of Puna[5]
　　　demands that I go

　　E hele au e—e hele au
　　I shall go—I shall go.

　　E hoʻopale au i ka lā o Haʻehaʻe e—
　　I shall ward off the sun of Haʻehaʻe[6]

　　ʻO ke koʻili a ka lā aia ma Puna
　　The rays of the sun shine down in Puna

　　Ma Puna ke aloha e—
(5)　At Puna is the love

　　Aloha wale.
　　Only love.

14　While he was chanting, one of his two *wāhine* whispered to the other, "The voice of our *kāne* is extremely skilled and beautiful when chanting."

15　"Perhaps it is important for this *kāne* of ours to chant at night," replied the other.

16　One of them shouted out with a loud voice, "O *Kāne*, you are really strange. One moment you are just sitting down there and then you get up and begin chanting."

17　"And what then is your complaint about what I am doing? Aren't your mouths stiff from talking too much?"

18　The second of the *wāhine* said, "You are right, *Kāne*; she is wrong."

19　The younger sister said to the elder sister, "What then is my mistake? This *kāne* of ours has left off the work for which he was first obtained, that is, the *ʻulumaika*[7] game."

5. *Puna* "Quadrangle and district, southeast Hawaiʻi" (PN) including Kīlauea volcano, where Pele lives.

6. *Haʻehaʻe* "Land division near Kumukahi. Makuʻu qd., Hawaiʻi" (PN). Kumukahi is the eastern-most point of Hawaiʻi. Haʻehaʻe is famous for being the place where the sun rises (Emerson 1915:189).

7. *ʻulumaika* This is a game similar to bowling, in which a round, polished stone is rolled over great distances and passes between two narrowly placed staves at the end of the course. The *ʻulumaika* stone is famous as a symbol of war (Kamakau 1961:150); Kahekili urged Kamehameha to wait for his death, and then said, "cast the *ʻulumaika*; it shall sweep the whole group of islands without obstruction" (Dibble 1843:49). This is the first instance I have seen where *ʻulumaika* is used as a sexual metaphor; however, *maika* formerly meant "to exercise violently; to be fatigued with hard exercise" (LAD).

20   "It seems that with that chant of yours, O *Kāne,* you are leaving us," said one of the two.

21   He did not reply, but instead dropped off to sleep. At dawn, the fire once again jabbed at his eyes. So he arose again and began to chant:

22   *Ke kiʻi mai nei ke ahi o ka pō iaʻu*
     The fires of the night come to fetch me

     E kono iaʻu e hele au
     Inviting me to come

     E hele au
     I shall go.

     ʻO kuʻu kino kai luhi
     It is my body that is tired.

     ʻO kaʻu wawae kai huʻi i ka hele
(5) It is my feet that ache in the walking

     E hele ana nō wau.
     I am going.

23   When one of his *wāhine* heard this chanting, she went to see Koea. Therefore, he came to meet with his son-in-law. Upon his arrival he asked,

24   "What is the reason for your insistence on going, my child?"

25   Kamapuaʻa answered, "There is fire, here in my eyes."

26   "Yes, it is a fire made by the woman,"[8] said the king.

27   "Can I then put out the fire?" asked Kamapuaʻa.

28   "You cannot put out this fire, because it is a fire from the night. If it was a fire made by man, then you could put it out."

29   Because of these words of Koea, Kamapuaʻa became very upset. Therefore, he jumped up and kissed[9] the noses of his *wāhine* and his father-in-law.

8. "The woman" refers to Pele, who seems to be famous even in Kahiki.

9. The Hawaiian **honi** was not a kiss with the lips but was "formerly, to touch noses on the side in greeting" (PED) or farewell.

30 "Don't go. Stay and rule your portion of land that you have just conquered, and become independent under our protection," said Koea, with the tears rolling down both his cheeks.

31 Kamapua'a said, "I cannot stay. I am going because my 'land'[10] is the journey."

32 His *wāhine* also tried to restrain him, but he would not listen, this pig-grandchild of Kamaunuaniho.

33 Kamapua'a finally turned to go and left his *wāhine*.

34 Your author is reminded of the old witty saying:

> *'O wau kā, ka ke aloha i luaiele ai*
> I am one indeed, who belongs to a
>   dissipating love

> *Ua kawewe wale i ke ala me ka waimaka*
> Tears just clatter upon the road like
>   a sudden downpour

> *'A'ohe wā a uku i nā hale.*
> In no time at all, there is payment in
>   the houses.

35 Therefore, this pig entered into the sea in his fish body, that is, *Nukunukuapua'a*.[11]

36 The time it took for Kamapua'a to return was faster than a steamship travels.

37 After four nights and four days, he landed at Ko'olina[12] in Waimānalo. He resumed his human body upon the land.

38 This one made his way until he arrived at Pu'u-o-Kapolei.[13] This is the hill mentioned in the name chant for the chiefess Pauahi,[14] who has passed away.

39 *Ia wahine hele lā o Kaiona*
This traveling woman of Kaiona[15]

> *Wahine hahai alualu Waili'ulā*
> The woman who pursues Waili'ulā[16]

10. Here *'āina,* or land, figuratively means "purpose." As one's purpose in life might be to control land (as was the chief's), the purpose of Kamapua'a was to journey.

11. *Nukunukuapua'a* Short form of *Humuhumu-nukunuku-ā-pua'a,* "Varieties of *humuhumu* (*Rhinecanthus aculeatus, R. rectangulus*). Lit., *humuhumu* with a snout like a pig" (PED). A fish *kinolau* of Kamapua'a.

12. *Ko'olina* A vacationing place for the chief Kākuhihewa at Waimānalo, a land division 'Ewa. The priest Nāpuaikama'o was the caretaker of this place (*Ke Au 'Oko'a,* July 13, 1910). Near Kalae-loa (Barber's Point), just south of Puu-o-Kapolei (Ii 1959:96). Note that there were two *ahupua'a* named Waimānalo on O'ahu; one in 'Ewa, and one in Ko'olaupoko.

13. *Pu'u-o-kapolei* Lit., hill of Kapolei, located at Honolulu, O'ahu (PN). Famous as the residence of the family of Kamapua'a. Kapolei may refer to Kapo, Pele's sister, or it may refer to an enchanted stone from Kaua'i (Beckwith 1970:52).

14. *Pauahi* Refers to Bernice Pauahi Bishop, who died in 1884.

15. *Kaiona* "Beach park, Waimānalo, O'ahu, said to be named for a benevolent relative of Pele" (PN). Probably in Waimānalo, 'Ewa. 21.20 North, 157.41 West (PSIC).

16. *Waili'ulā* Lit., mirage. It is capitalized in the original text, and I presume that it is a proper name or a place.

Pua ‘Ōhai o ke Kaha
An *‘ōhai*[17] flower of the shore

‘Uhane kui pua lei o Kamau-a
A spirit that strings flower *lei*
    at Kamau-a[18]

(5)   *‘U‘umi ia iho ke aloha o ke kāne*
      Held back inside is the love of the *kāne*

Ua inaina, ua manawa ‘ino
Angry, bad feelings

Nona ka nā hale i pu‘u o Kapolei
For her are the houses at Pu‘u-o-Kapolei

Ke nonoho ala no me nā wāhine o ka ma‘o.
Living there with the women of the green.[19]

40   Kamapua‘a arrived at Pu‘u-o-Kapolei, and there
     met with all his relatives.

41   They lived comfortably together, day and night
     for several weeks [*anahulu*].

42   While they were sleeping one night, Pele again
     came to fetch him, jabbing at his eyes. And he
     began to chant:

43   *Ke ki‘i mai nei ke ahi a ke Akua wahine o
        Puna ia‘u e kono—*
     The fires of the female *Akua* of Puna[20] have
        come to fetch me, enticing me

E hele au e—e hele au
I shall go—I shall go

E ho‘opale au i ka lā o Ha‘eha‘e e—
I shall ward off the sun of Ha‘eha‘e[21]

‘O ke ko‘ili a ka lā aia ma Puna
The rays of the sun shine down in Puna

(5)   *Ma Puna ke aloha e—*
      At Puna is the love

Aloha wale.
Only love.

17. *‘ōhai* "A native legume (*Sesbania tomentosa*), a low to prostrate shrub with hairy, pale leaves and red or orange, inch-long flowers" (PED). This flower is often used in love chants as a pun on *ho‘oha‘i, lit.*, to flirt (PED).

18. *Kamau-a* This seems to be a place name but it is not listed in PN, SO, PSIC, or on Bier's 1977 map, so perhaps it has been lost.

19. Refers to *Wahine‘ōma‘o,* the traveling companion of Hi‘iaka. For some reason, Wahine-‘ōma‘o is associated with Pu‘u-o-kapolei, and later in this story she will be the companion of the grandmother of Kamapua‘a. The story behind her name seems lost to us today.

20. See note 5.

21. See note 6.

44 The grandmother said, "Perhaps then you should go. But you should remember while you are there that this indeed is the fire that will scorch your pig bristles."

45 "Perhaps then she will 'touch' me, and as for me, the pig will certainly 'touch' her."

46 His grandmother said, "You should sleep. Don't rush off because the fire has come to fetch you. This is a real fire. It's a fire with teeth."[22]

47 So he dropped off to sleep again. The fire came to fetch him again, and he chanted once more:

48 *Ke ki'i mai nei ke ahi o ka pō ia'u e kono ia'u, e kono ia'u*
The fires of the night come to fetch me, enticing me

E hele au—e hele au
I shall go—I shall go.

'O ku'u kino kai luhi
It is my body that is tired.

'O ka'u wawae ua hu'i i ka hele
(5) It is my feet that ache in the walking

E hele ana nō wau.
I am going.

E ho'okō i ka 'i'ini a loko.
To fulfill the inner desire.

49 Upon the morning of the next day, he said to his grandmother, his parents, and his elder brothers . . .

It is not finished.

22. A reference to *'anā'anā*. See *niho* in PED.

Aole I Pau

KAMAPUA'A RETURNS TO O'AHU

AND CONTINUES TO HAWAI'I

ISSUE 9

1   "You folks should remain on our land here, because it was conquered by me a long time ago at the Pillars of Kahiki.

2   "I shall swim again in the sea until I arrive at the island of the fire that has come so frequently to fetch me. So I shall prepare myself for my journey."

3   Then he turned and said to his first-born brother,[1] to Kekeleiʻaikū, "Listen to me, elder brother. You wait here. When you smell the stench of burning bristles, then you must assume I am dead. However, if indeed you do not smell the stench of the bristles, you will know that your younger brother has not been harmed and that he has 'eaten of the cooked taro.'"[2]

4   When he finished speaking to his elder brother, he turned and questioned his grandmother. "Here I am about to go, and shall I then go alone?"

5   "What is the use of going alone, as perhaps a child without parents or indeed as a child without grandparents? Therefore, when you go, go together with your grandparents. What then shall they do, waiting here behind, while you, 'the bloody bones,'[3] go off there? Because they are your servants,[4] and upon your command they will be there to obey you. And as for the one who does not obey your command, drive him away from your presence."

6   Right after Kamaunuaniho had finished speaking . . . [4 lines of this paragraph are illegible because the newspaper was damaged] and the family was behind, swimming in the sea for the island of Hawaiʻi.[5]

7   "You go," said the grandmother, "and your grandparents shall follow afterward. You shall all meet together at Hawaiʻi; that is the place you desire."

1. In actuality, Kahikihonuakele was the first-born, but Kamapuaʻa addresses Kekeleiʻaikū in this manner out of affection.

2. *Ke ʻai ala no ʻo ia i kalo moʻa* Fig., was victorious. *ʻAi no i kalo moʻa* (one can eat cooked taro); the work is done; one can sit at ease and enjoy himself (ON 83).

3. *ka ʻiwi koko* Since ʻiwi, or bones, refers to life, 'bloody bones' is equivalent to the English slang "a live body." See also Issue 1, note 39; Issue 4, notes 1, 9; Issue 6, note 14; and Issue 7, note 13. *He iwi koko* (blooded bones); a living person (ON 646).

4. Again the term is *kauwā-lawelawe* (as in Issue 7, note 14) and may imply that the grandparents of Kamapuaʻa should be his servants.

5. *Hawaiʻi* "Largest island in the Hawaiian group, 76 miles wide, 93 miles long, with an area of 4,030 square miles" (PN). Island home of Pele.

8   Therefore, they gave their very last farewells, and Kamapuaʻa descended from Puʻu-o-Kapolei until he arrived by the sea of Kualakaʻi.[6]

9   Then he changed his human body into his fish body. This day became night and this night became day. Then he landed at the place called Pōhakuʻou[7] at Kohala,[8] Hawaiʻi.

10 Upon his landing, he changed to human form once again. He saw several women picking ʻopihi[9] and also gathering seaweed.

11 This one went there and gave his *aloha* to them, and the women responded in a similar manner.

12 "Arenʻt you two cold walking out here on the beach in the early morning?" said Kamapuaʻa.

13 "It is cold. But perhaps patience will obtain us a small morning meal. There is nothing at all to eat for those who sit at home. 'Just looking in someone else's meat dish,'"[10] said the woman.

14 "Yes, thatʻs true. Yet isnʻt your beach rather jagged and rocky?"

15 "Yes, it is rocky. Indeed, it would be better for all of us to return to the house to eat."

16 "I am not hungry," said Kamapuaʻa.

17 "And where have you come from?" said the women.

18 "I am from right here, and I shall travel far beyond this place," said Kamapuaʻa.

19 "Do you two perhaps have some water?"

20 "We donʻt have any water, and you will see us brushing off the dew upon the leaves of the ʻilima;[11] that is the bathing water of this land. This land is called 'the waterless plain where only ʻilima flowers grow in the sun,'[12] because this is a waterless land.

6. *Kualakaʻi* "Area near Barber's Point, Oʻahu . . . *Lit., Tethys* (a sea creature)" (PN). It can also be translated as "to rise up and lead."

7. *Pōhakuʻou* Seems to be a lost place name. Not listed in PN, PSIC, or on Bier's 1976 map. *Lit.,* "the thrusting rock."

8. *Kohala* "District . . . north-west Hawaiʻi" (PN).

9. *ʻopihi* "Limpet, any of several species of *Helcioniscus*" (PED).

10. *he nānā i ka haʻi ipukai* Meaning they often look to other people for food.

11. *ʻilima* "Small to large native shrubs (all species of *Sida*, especially *S. fallax*), bearing yellow, orange, greenish, or dull-red flowers; some kinds strung for leis. The flowers last only a day and are so delicate that about 500 are needed for one lei" (PED).

12. *ʻIlima kula wai ʻole i ka lā* Said here to be a reference to Pōhakuʻou, Kohala, but seems unknown today. *Ola nā ʻilima wai ʻole i ke ao ʻōpua* (healed are the ʻilima of waterless places by the rain cloud) (ON 2487).

21 "But if you desire a different kind of 'water,'[13] we can quickly get it. We will give it as a gift to you without any delay. It is a bubbling spring. It's here 'in the bosom of Hoʻohila,'[14] making sweet noises.

22 "First we shall drink of the real water, and afterward we shall drink of the 'refreshing water.' Then we can dwell in the darkness of the *palai*[15] ferns."

23 Then this Kamapuaʻa of ours turned, and his hands reached out into the sea. The springwater surged up into the sea.

24 So water was found, and the name of this spring was called Kīpū.[16]

25 "You two come and fill up your water gourd in order to get some water for all of us."

26 These women came to scoop up the water, and they drank deeply.

27 When they were finished, Kamapuaʻa said to the women, "You two said there was no water, yet here there is water. Perhaps you just didn't look for it."

28 These women said, "This has been a waterless land from ancient times, and it was you who found this source of water.

29 "This is a wondrous thing. We have lived here since the days of our youth up until now, when we have become mature adults. The desire for water has been very great, and now the water of this land has been found.

30 "We are very happy and we bless and praise you with a great many thanks, for your searching here for the water of this land."

13. This 'water' is the wetness of lovemaking. The 'bubbling spring' in this same paragraph is symbolic of the female genital.

14. *i ka poli o Hoʻohila* Hoʻohila means "suffusion of the face; a blushing of the face" (LAD), here personified to figuratively mean a lover.

15. *palai* "A native fern (*Microlepia setosa*), growing wild and cultivated, three to four feet high. The lacy ovate fronds look much like those of the *palaʻa* but are somewhat hairy instead of smooth" (PED). The *palai* fern is used in many love chants and seems to symbolize pubic hair.

16. *Kīpū Lit.*, to hold back (PED). Said to be a spring in Kauaʻi made by Kamapuaʻa (Kahiolo 1978:122), but it is not known as a place name in Kohala. Not found in PN, PSIC, or on Bier's 1976 map. The *kaona* here is that Kamapuaʻa, as the eternal lover, makes wet the female earth and brings forth springwater, as did the God Kāne, another ancient male symbol.

31 Thereafter, Kamapuaʻa became excited[17] at the thought of making love[18] with these women. This has reminded the author of a beloved name chant for the chiefs:

32 *Hōʻeu ka polopua a ka Waiʻōpua, ʻōpua e—*
The pandanus flower of the Waiʻōpua[19]
rises up, a cloud.

He aha lā ka mea lena i ka uka o Kahiʻu?
What is that thing stretching out in the
uplands of Kahiʻu?[20]

He kuahine lāua me ke kiowao
They two are the *kuahine*[21] rain, and
the cool mountain rain[22]

*He mau koko ka ʻāpeʻapeʻa hili ia
i luna o ka lāʻau*
The *ʻāpeʻapeʻa*[23] entwined above
the trees are rainbows

Ke hoʻokahekahe aʻela i kai o ʻEwa.
Flowing into the sea of ʻEwa.[24]

33 At this place where Kamapuaʻa did these things 'pertaining to the body,'[25] the name of these following places have been called from that time until this time, Huʻalua,[26] that is, the foaming at the mouth of Kamapuaʻa.

34 Kealahewa[27] was the excess of the eyes and mouth of Kamapuaʻa. ʻOpihipaʻū[28] was the one who clung to Kamapuaʻa.

35 After the traveler caught his breath, he gave his final farewell and went straight along the road to Kona.[29]

17. *hōʻeu* "To stir up, incite, animate, encourage, bestow" (PED). *Fig.*, to get an erection. See *Ko maʻi Hoʻeuʻeu* (Elbert and Mahoe 1970:67).

18. The actual term is *hui kino*, lit., to join bodies.

19. *Waiʻōpua* "Name of a pleasant breeze. Lit., water of cloud banks" (PED). "The pandanus flower of this breeze that rises up (*hoʻeu*) refers to Kamapuaʻa. The male flower of the pandanus (*hinano*), when dried, was sprinkled upon a lover as a love charm" (Handy and Handy 1972:201).

20. *Kahiʻu* "Point, Kalaupapa peninsula, Molokaʻi. Lit., the fish tail" (PN).

21. *Kuahine* "Name of a rain in Mānoa valley, Oʻahu" (PED). *Lit.*, "a sister of a brother" (LAD).

22. The cool mountain rain and the *kuahine* rain refer to the two sisters that Kama met on the beach.

23. *ʻāpeʻapeʻa* "Same as *peʻapeʻa*, the bat" (PED). This meaning does not seem to fit, but there are no other relevant meanings in LAD or PED.

24. *ʻEwa* "Quadrangle west of Pearl Harbor, Oʻahu. *Lit.*, crooked" (PN). District including Hālawa in the east and all land to Honouliuli in the west (SO map of ʻEwa).

25. *hana pilikino Fig.*, made love.

26. *Huʻalua Lit.*, foaming twice, as he had made love twice.

27. *Kealahewa Lit.*, the satiating path. A name of one of the sisters, which puns upon *hewa*, meaning excess.

28. *ʻOpihipaʻū Lit.*, moist *ʻopihi. ʻOpihi* is a kind of limpet that clings with remarkable strength to rocks. The names of these sisters are puns on the act of lovemaking.

29. *Kona* This Kona refers to the leeward district of Hawaiʻi.

36 On the evening of this day, he arrived at the
    district of Ka'ū.[30] Ka'ū is the land; 'Ahukini[31]
    is the water; there at Kamā'oa[32] is the cliff of
    Mōlilele.[33]

37 He visited houses of the natives. The natives saw
    this fine man standing outside, and their call
    was heard for this one to enter and join with
    the natives. It was similar to this sweet call:

38   *'O wau mai kau e hea mai ai*
        It is I who am calling to you

        E hea i ke kanaka e komo ma loko
        Calling to the person to come inside

        E hānai ai a hewa a'e ka waha
        To eat until the mouth can hold no more

        Eia no ka uku lā o ka leo.
        Here is the reward of the voice.

39 This is in keeping with the eternal custom
    of this Nation. This is a race that calls out to
    people with open hearts. That is the way natives
    greet their new friends.

40 Whereupon Kamapua'a called out to his grand-
    parents to hide themselves in his secret place.[34]
    His grandparents then fulfilled his command.

41 Then the natives prepared those things that
    would comfort the body [food], and their eating
    mats were laden down with food.

42 Kamapua'a ate with a great appetite, until he
    had had enough of the generosity of the natives.
    He slept there on this night.

43 When it was dawn, the natives arose first to
    prepare their eating mats for the morning.

44 When this one arose, the natives were waiting
    for him. After their meal was finished, he gave
    his last farewells and his thanks for their
    generosity to him. And he said . . .

It is not finished.

30. *Ka'ū* District and desert in the southern portion of Hawai'i (PN). *Lit.,* the breast. Notice that when Kamapua'a journeyed to Kīlauea, he traveled in a counterclockwise direction, which is a portent of bad luck.

31. *'Ahukini* "Lava tube shelter and pool, formerly called Wai-o-'Ahukini, on the Kona side of South Point, Hawai'i. . . . *Lit.,* water [of] 'Ahukini (a super-natural woman)" (PN).

32. *Kamā'oa* "Plain near Ka Lae (South Point), Ka'ū, Hawai'i, a place noted for red dust" (PN).

33. *Mōlilele* "Cliff inland of Wai-o-'Ahukini, Hawai'i. *Lit.,* leaping albatross" (PN).

34. *wahi huna* *Fig.,* the genitals.

KAMAPUA'A AWAKENS PELE

ISSUE 10

1   "I have nothing with which to repay your matchless generosity."

2   The natives answered, "Don't concern yourself with these things. It is nothing. Perhaps the desire to go visiting at your place may arise among us. Then you will receive the natives of this place."

3   Kamapua'a said, "This is a good thing. Our place is on the island of O'ahu, in a section of Kona.[1] If the idea to travel to O'ahu should grow, our house is for visiting, and we shall be living there as natives."

4   Kamapua'a became a fine person in the natives' opinion. He gave his last farewells to them and continued on his journey. He traveled on until he arrived at Kapāpala.[2] This place was Keanapua'a,[3] and they lay down there to sleep.

5   His grandfather, that is, Kūliaikekaua, arose and said, "Here we are sleeping. We should go on while it's not too dark." So Kamapua'a arose and they all went on until that time when it was completely dark, until they reached 'Ōhi'aokalani.[4]

6   When dawn broke, they traveled again until Akanikōlea,[5] and they rested there, waiting for the day to break.

7   But Kūliaikekaua said to his grandchild, "It would be better for us to descend below to Pele there. We should attack at night in order that 'our skin doesn't know the pain.'[6] She will be startled. We shall be united and their household will be filled with panic.

8   "Thus we should proceed. Therefore, hear and obey, O my grandchild, this counsel of your grandparent to you. If we should do this, we shall vanquish Pele."

1. *Kona* Old name for a district of O'ahu, now known as Honolulu, formerly included all the land from Kuli'ou'ou to Moanalua. Note that this is *not* where Kamapua'a's family lived, so he had no intention of returning their hospitality.

2. *Kapāpala* "Land section, Kīlauea and Mauna Loa qds., Hawai'i. Lit., the *Charpentiera* shrub" (PN).

3. *Keanapua'a* Lit., the pig's cave. Not found in PN, PSIC, or on Bier's 1976 map, although here it is said to be in Kapāpala.

4. *'Ōhi'aokalani* Lit., [the] 'Ōhi'a (*Metrosideros*) tree of the chief. Seems to be a lost place name, as it is not found in PN, PSIC, or on Bier's 1976 map.

5. *Akanikōlea* "Land near Kīlauea Crater, Hawai'i, where Kamapua'a taunted Pele. . . . Lit., plover cry" (PN); *fig.*, where the stranger calls out.

6. *i'ole kākou e 'ike ka 'ili i ka 'eha* *Fig.*, so they would not be hurt or defeated. Ka'ōleiokū said to 'Umi, "'*a'ole e 'eha i ka ili*," lit., "the skin will not know the pain," which is a prophecy regarding 'Umi's battle with Lonoapi'ilani (For. Col. 4:246). Similar to *Ua 'eha ka 'ili i ka maka o ka ihe*, the skin has been hurt by the point of the spear (ON 2775).

9   Kamapua'a said, "That is indeed the way a warrior becomes known. If we were all boys, we might say to ourselves that we should proceed like that. Then again it might perhaps be said by others that we are just cowards.

10 "Therefore, let us wait until it is day, when Pele shall awaken with her eyes open. She shall see us, and we shall delight in each other's presence. This is my command for you all to obey."

11 At these words of Kamapua'a, Kūliaikekaua put an end to his thoughts, but he spoke again. "There's a little house standing there below, which is full of people. Let me go inside and disturb them."

12 "This is the way known by you, a warrior. Meeting face to face, fleeing and fleeing, death and death, victory and victory. You all must hide in my hidden place⁷ and disappear lest Pele see you."

13 Kūliaikekaua said, "Pele's people shall awaken to see us among the many people below." Then he began to chant:

14   *'Oi kapakapa aku*
        Summoning the best

        'Oi ho'oko'oko'ona
        Exceedingly supportive

        'Oi hoainu 'awa
        The best *'awa*-drinking companions

        Make Lehu
        The multitudes die

        Kūliaikekaua
(5)   Striving in the war

        Kūliaikai
        Striving in the sea

        Kūliaiuka
        Striving in the uplands

7. *ko'u wahi huna* Refers to his genitals.

Kūmahumahukole[8]
Wretched scoundrel

'O Kaleka'aka[9]
O watery reflection

'O nā Akua ho'ohaumia o Kamapua'a.
(10)   O the defiling *Akua* of Kamapua'a.

15   At this time the grandparents of Kamapua'a
descended with great force upon his body and
changed him into a handsome man, more beautiful than any of Pele's people. Thereafter, he
asked his grandfathers, "How does my appearance look to you now?"

16   His grandparents answered, "How indeed! It is
by your body that you will be known by Pele
and her younger sisters. Upon their awakening
they shall be entranced by you, the beautiful
young man. Therefore, let Pele be awakened."
Then Kamapua'a chanted again:

17   *'O ke ahi a Lonomakua*
O the fire of Lonomakua[10]

A ko'u Akua a Pele
Of Pele, my *Akua*

Ke ala i ka uka o Hāmākualoa
The path is upland of Hāmākualoa[11]

'O ka haukea o Maunakea
O the snow of Mauna Kea[12]

'O ka'uahi po'okea aia i luna
(5)   O the ash-colored smoke there above

'O ka wahine leo nui i ka uka o Koa'ekea
O the woman with the great voice in the
uplands of Koa'ekea[13]

'O ke ahi po'okea aia i ka Lani
O the ash-colored fire there in the heavens

Hālāwai 'ia e ka'u mau lani
Met by my chiefs

8. *Kūmahumahukole* This is said
to be "an epithet of sarcasm
applied to his opponent; creaking
and cracking, referring to his
boastings." Kamapua'a chanting
to Lonoka'eho (For. Col. 5:331).
Here it is the name of a '*defiling
Akua*' of Kamapua'a.

9. *'O Kaleka'aka* Although
said here to be a defiling *Akua*
of Kamapua'a, it may be a form
of *O kole ka aka*, (of *kole* the
laughter), the last line of a chant
by Kamapua'a to Lonoka'eho
(For. Col. 5:331).

10. *Lonomakua* "An uncle of
Pele's, who brought fire at her
command. . . . He kept the sacred
fire of the underworld under his
armpit. The *makahiki* image bore
his name. . . . *Lit.*, elder Lono"
(PED 393).

11. *Hāmākualoa* This refers to
the district of northeast Hawai'i.

12. *Mauna Kea* "Highest
mountain in Hawai'i (13,796 feet).
. . . *Lit.*, white mountain (often the
mountain is snowcapped)" (PN).

13. *Koa'ekea* *Lit.*, white tropic
bird. Not listed in PN or PSIC, but
Emerson (1909:67) lists Koa'ekea
as a cliff on the side of Waipi'o
Valley, Hawai'i. However, this
may not be the one referred to
in this chant.

He Akua ulupuni
An *Akua* overcome with emotion

(10) *Ulu ma ka nāhelehele*
Inspired in the forest

He Akua pāhaʻohaʻo
An *Akua* with puzzling bodies

ʻO Lono lā ka maka
Lono[14] is the favorite

ʻO Waia lā ke kaula
Waia[15] is the prophet

Ke ʻupu mai nei iaʻu e ʻai i ke kanaka
I long to eat the people

(15) *ʻO waimaka nui*
O great tears

Hiolo ka leo o ka pōhaku
Falling is the voice of the rock

ʻUwē hone ka leo o ka Alakaʻi ke—, kani ke—
The voice of the leader cries sweetly, calling

Aweaweʻula ka leo o Kamāmane
Faint is the voice of Kamāmane[16]

Kōī waimaka nui
Great tears are overflowing

Ke kau ka hōkū i Hanakahi
(20) The star hangs at Hanakahi[17]

Pau Kīlauea i ke ahi
Kīlauea[18] is consumed by the fire

Kunia ihola wela ka pōhaku
Searing heat, the rocks are burning

Haoa ke ʻā lele i luna
Scorching is the lava flowing above

Pākuʻi, ʻawaʻawa, kenakena ka ʻuwahi a ke
  Akua wahine
Heavily scented, bitter, stifling is the smoke
  of the female *Akua*

14. *Lono* "One of the four great *akuas* . . . considered an *akua* of clouds, winds, the sea, agriculture, and fertility. . . . He was the patron of the annual *makahiki* festival" (PED 392).

15. *Waia* A son of Hāloa who "was extremely corrupt. He was so absorbed in the pursuit of pleasure that he disregarded the instructions of his father to pray to the gods, to look well after the affairs of the kingdom, and to take good care of his people so that the country might be prosperous" (Malo 1951:244). This may refer to another *Waia*.

16. *Kamāmane* Lit., the *māmane* tree (*Sophora chrysophylla*). *Fig.,* "Attractive, said of a person sexually appealing but not necessarily good-looking, perhaps so called because of the attractive flower of the *māmane* tree" (PED).

17. *Hanakahi* "A land on the Hāmākua side of Hilo, also a king whose name was a synonym for profound peace" (Emerson 1909:60).

18. *Kīlauea* "Active volcano on the flank of Mauna Loa, nearly continuously active 1823–1894 and 1907–1924; eruptions began again in 1952 and still continue. . . . Lit., spewing, much spreading (referring to volcanic eruptions)" (PN).

'O Puna o Pele lā e—ala ho'i

(25) O Puna, O Pele—indeed awaken!

E ala mai 'oe au e moe loa nei
Awake from your long sleep

No ke aha no lā ho'i ka moe loa 'ana?
For what then is the long sleep?

Ala mai ho'i!
Indeed, awaken!

18   Then the people of Pele's front and the people
of Pele's back[19] awoke, these Pele people arose
and their eyes looked above. Therefore, Kūliaikekaua called out, "O Kama, Pele's people of the
front have awakened. Pele's people of the back
have awakened. Remaining are those
people of the ends of the house, of the middle,
and of the rooftop. These are Pele's people
that remain. Therefore, let all be awakened."
Then, this one chanted again:

19   *Mai Hawai'i, mai Puna*
From Hawai'i, from Puna,

Mai Kīlauea, mai Wahinekapu
From Kīlauea, from Wahinekapu[20]

Mai O'oluea
From O'oluea[21]

Aneane ha'alele wale i Puna
Almost to the end of Puna

I 'ōneanea i kai o Pu'ulena
(5) Desolate is the land seaward of Pu'ulena[22]

I Kama a Kamalama
At Kama of Ka Malama[23]

Ha'a i kou lili, o Kūliaikekaua, o Kama e—
Humbled is your pride, O Kūliaikekaua,
    O Kama

Popo'i i kou 'ō, he 'ō ai 'āina
Covered is your spear, a spear that makes
    love to the land

19. *Kā Pele o ke alo, kā Pele o ke kua* Lit., those belonging to Pele of the front, those belonging to Pele of the back. This may perhaps be an allusion to parts of the house, because Halema'uma'u, the name of Pele's home and the crater itself, means a house thatched with *'ama'u* fern.

20. *Wahinekapu* ". . . a bluff in the north-western wall that surrounds the caldera of Kilauea, the tabu residence of god Ka-mo-ho-alii, a brother of Pele" (Emerson 1915:140). Lit., the sacred woman, referring to Pele.

21. *O'oluea* Seems to be a lost place name; not found in PN, PSIC, or on Bier's 1976 map.

22. *Pu'ulena* A pit crater at Malama-uka, Kalapana, Hawai'i, where Pele is said to have tried to make her home. As she dug she encountered water, and so moved on to Kīlauea (Green 1923:21; PN). Also, the "name of a famous cold wind at Kīlauea, Hawai'i" (PED).

23. *Malama* "Inland crater, sea area, land section, and home-steads, Kalapana qd., Hawai'i. . . . Lit., month or moon" (PN).

I ka uka o Maunaloa, ma uka o Kaʻū
Upland of Mauna Loa,[24] upland of Kaʻū

Ke hea ka wā ala i lalo o Halemaʻumaʻu
(10)   Calling, roaring there below at
     Halemaʻumaʻu[25]

Ua piha kuʻi o Maunakea
Maunakea is packed full

He mea ʻē o Kalaeloa
Kalaeloa[26] is extraordinary

He mea ʻē o Kalaʻapoko
Kalaʻapoko[27] is unusual

Ua heʻe hoʻi nā puʻu nui ʻelua
The two large hills are also flowing

He ʻelua hoʻi wai ʻulaʻula
(15)   There are also two red waters

He ʻelua hoʻi wai welawela
There are also two hot springs

He ʻelua hoʻi mau loko iʻa
There are also two fish ponds

He mōhāhā, he puʻu Onekea
Spreading widely, Onekea[28] is a hill

He puʻuwai o Onekea
Onekea is the heart

Hāwele aulana o Kaulanamauna
(20)   Kaulanamauna[29] is tied on gently

Hulihia aku ana
Completely overturning

ʻEhia auheʻe o ka nalu?
How many times have the waves
   been dispersed?

Ou aliʻi wahine o Puna
You chiefly woman of Puna

ʻO Pele lā, e ala hoʻi
O Pele there, indeed, awaken!

24. *Mauna Loa* "Active volcano, second highest mountain in Hawaiʻi . . . central Hawaiʻi . . . *lit.,* long mountain" (PN).

25. *Halemaʻumaʻu Lit.,* house of ʻamaʻu *(Sadleria)* fern. "Crater (3,646 feet elevation), also known as the fire pit, within the larger Kīlauea Crater" (PN). The home of Pele (Emerson 1909:200). Also *fig.* the *maʻi* of Pele as in the *mele maʻi* (genital chant) "E Komo Maloko o Halemaʻumaʻu."

26. *Kalaeloa Lit.,* the long peninsula. A point along the Puna coast in the *ahupuaʻa* of Kamaili at 19.25 North, 154.54 West (Hawaii Territorial Survey map 1902, PSIC). Not listed in PN.

27. *Kalaʻapoko* Seems to be a lost place name; not found in PN, PSIC, or on Bier's 1976 map. *Lit.,* the short sanctity.

28. *Onekea Lit.,* white sands. Seems to be another lost place name; not found in PN, PSIC, or on Bier's 1976 map.

29. *Kaulanamauna* "Land section, Hoʻōpūloa qd., South Kona, Hawaiʻi; there was food here, and it was a place where mountain travelers rested. *Lit.,* mountain resting place" (PN).

E ala mai 'oe e moe loa nei
(25) Awaken you who sleeps so long

No ke aha no lā ka moe loa 'ana?
For what then is this long sleep?

E ala mai ho'i!
Indeed, awaken!

E ala ho'i e Halema'uma'u!
Indeed, awaken, O Halema'uma'u!

E ala ho'i e ka poukua
Awaken also, O back posts

E ala ho'i e ka poualo
(30) Awaken also, O front posts

E ala ho'i e kēlā kala
Awaken also, O that gable

E ala ho'i e kēia kala
Awaken also, O this gable

E ala e Hi'iaka-i-ka-'ale-'ī
Awaken, O Hi'iaka-i-ka-'ale-'ī[30]

E ala e Hi'iaka-i-ka-'ale-'moe
Awaken, O Hi'iaka-i-ka-'ale-moe[31]

E ala e Hi'iaka-i-ka-'ale kualono
(35) Awaken, O Hi'iaka-i-ka-'ale-kualono[32]

E ala e Hi'iaka wāwāhilani
Awaken, O Hi'iaka-wāwāhilani[33]

E ala e Hi'iaka-i-ka pua māmane
Awaken, O Hi'iaka-i-ka-pua-māmane[34]

E ala e Hi'iaka-i-ka pua hā'ena'ena
Awaken, O Hi'iaka-i-ka-pua-hā'ena'ena[35]

E ala e Hi'iaka-i-ka pua Ko'olau
Awaken, O Hi'iaka-i-ka-pua-ko'olau[36]

E ala e Hi'iaka Pu'ule'ule
(40) Awaken, O Hi'iaka-Pu'ule'ule[37]

E ala e Hi'iaka pā pūlehu
Awaken, O Hi'iaka-pā-pūlehu[38]

30. *Hi'iaka-i-ka-'ale 'ī* "A Hi'iaka sister. *Lit.*, Hi'iaka in the giant billow (perhaps a reference to tidal waves)" (PED 383). She is usually mentioned first in the list of Hi'iaka sisters (Emerson 1915:222). Alternatively, the reference to waves may mean waves of molten lava, which look like a flowing sea when erupting.

31. *Hi'iaka-i-ka-'ale-moe* "A Hi'iaka sister. *Lit.*, Hi'iaka in the low-lying billow" (PED 383).

32. *Hi'iaka-i-ka-'ale-kualono* A Hi'iaka sister, as are all the following persons whose names begin with Hi'iaka. *Lit.*, Hi'iaka in the overturning wave.

33. *Hi'iaka-wāwāhilani* *Lit.*, Hi'iaka who bursts the heavens.

34. *Hi'iaka-i-ka-pua-māmane* *Lit.*, Hi'iaka in the *māmane* (*Sophora chrysophylla*) flower. See Issue 10, note 15.

35. *Hi'iaka-i-ka-pua-hā'ena'ena* *Lit.*, Hi'iaka in the burning red flower. "Her emblem was the little bud-like pea blossom flame" (Emerson 1915:222).

36. *Hi'iaka-i-ka-pua-ko'olau* *Lit.*, Hi'iaka in the *ko'olau* (*Bidens* spp.) flower.

37. *Hi'iaka-Pu'ule'ule* Pu'ule'ule may be a form of *pū'ulī'ulī*, "a variety of small gourd, as used for making feather gourd rattles ('ulī'ulī), medicine cups ('apu), and individual *poi* containers" (PED). With this meaning, the name would be Hi'iaka of the gourd.

38. *Hi'iaka-pā-pūlehu* *Lit.*, Hi'iaka whose touch scorches.

E ala e Hiʻiaka ai mīana
Awaken, O Hiʻiaka-ʻai-mīana[39]

E ala e Hiʻiaka noho lae
Awaken, O Hiʻiaka-noho-lae[40]

E ala e Hiʻiaka i ka poli o Pele
Awaken, O Hiʻiaka-i-ka-poli-o-Pele[41]

E ala mai hoʻi
(45)   Indeed, awaken!

E ala mai ʻoe e moe loa nei
Awaken, you who sleep so long

No ke aha no lā hoʻi ʻoe e moe loa nei?
For what then indeed is this long sleep?

It is not finished.

39. *Hiʻiaka-ʻai-mīana* Lit., Hiʻiaka who eats at or rules the urinal.

40. *Hiʻiaka-noho-lae* Lit., Hiʻiaka who dwells in the peninsula. "She was recognized by a trickle of blood on the forehead" (Emerson 1915:222).

41. *Hiʻiaka-i-ka-poli-o-Pele* Lit., Hiʻiaka in the bosom of Pele. "Pele's favorite younger sister born from the mouth of Haumea. . . . Born as an egg, she was carried under Pele's bosom until she became a young beauty" (PED 303). Hence the name.

PELE'S SISTERS

DESIRE KAMAPUA'A

ISSUE 11

1   At this time, people emerged from within the house, and the bottom of the crater was filled by a great number of people. Then Kūliaikekaua said, "O Kama, look, the people have come and are gathering together."

2   When Kamapuaʻa looked, there were more people than he had ever seen. The house standing below was so small, yet here the number of people was ʻ40,000 and 400,000.'[1] Then he said to his grandfathers, "I had only heard of the great number of Pele's warriors. This is the first time I have seen them with my very own eyes. Pele is only weak and lovely. Therefore, let us all begin[2] this war."

3   Kamapuaʻa stood above at Akanikōlea. The people below saw this handsome man standing above. They all shouted out with a loud voice, "Indeed, that one is the most virile[3] of all the beautiful youths. There is no other like him in Hawaiʻi."

4   Some of the younger sisters of Pele ran to tell Pele about that handsome man standing above at Akanikōlea. "You should see him. The touch of your kapu skin will free him, then we will make him a kāne for all of us, the beautiful young women.[4] Thereafter, we will be the companions who can really satisfy his trembling.[5] What do you think of this idea, O our first-born sister?"

5   "Don't you all mistakenly think, my younger sisters, that he's a real man. That is not a man, but a pig, standing there above at Akanikōlea. There, he seems to be a man, ready ʻto make love in the bosom of Hoʻohila.'[6]

1. *he mau kini a lehu* Kini, "forty thousand," *lehu*, "400,000" (PED). This does not refer to the actual number of people but is a saying meaning a great many or numerous and usually refers to the great number of *Akua* in the Hawaiian pantheon. Perhaps all of Pele's people were *Akua*.

2. The term used is *hoaʻo*, which actually means "to try."

3. The term used is *koʻu*, "conception; male potency" (PED). Contextually, it seems to mean virile or masculine.

4. As was customary for Pele and her sisters, one *kāne* would be shared by all, but only after Pele had ʻfreed the *kapu*' by taking him as her lover first. So it was proposed by Pele with regard to Lohiʻau, her famous chiefly lover from Kauaʻi. After she had enjoyed him for five days and nights, the other sisters could have him (Emerson 1915:8, 15).

5. The term is *naue*, "to move, shake, tremble; to quake, as the earth; to vibrate; to march . . . revolving, as hips in a hula" (PED). *Naue* is used in many genital chants to describe lovemaking.

6. *ke kaunu ana i ka poli o Hoʻohila* Hoʻohila is a personification of blushing. See Issue 9, note 14. Not found in ON.

6   "You must heed me, O younger sisters—a pig and human women! Is that then a suitable match for lovemaking? Therefore, don't you mistakenly desire that man standing above, looking as though he were a real man. He is thought to be a man, not a hairy pig. These are truly ignorant thoughts of yours, younger sisters. You would only be wasting your fine bodies, thinking he is a man who will 'preserve the bones.' Don't be stubborn, O younger sisters, with your questioning thoughts. I am not forbidding you, O younger sisters, but I know what is the true worth of this man."

7   One of them said, "You are such a good liar. We can see with our own eyes the appearance of that beautiful young man. Yet it is denied by you. Perhaps you just want our *kāne* all to yourself."

8   "That is not what I think! If a *kāne* is had by me, he is for all of you. And also, if one is had by you, he is shared equally with all of us. Perhaps it would not be so bad to think of him as our *kāne*. Perhaps you should ask him, from whence does this hairy man, who violates our sacred mountain, come."

9   Then they inquired of him as their first-born sister had instructed them.

10   The grandfather of Kamapua'a answered, "It is supposed that he is from the seashore of Puna, from the place which Pele often frequents as a native by the seaside."

11   *Ua 'ike ho'i au i kēnā kanikani*
Indeed, I know that roaring sound

   Kau i luna o ka Lehua
Placed upon the *lehua*[7] flower

   Hewa ka wawae i ka loa o ke ā
The feet trip upon the length of rough lava

   Ke hele ma uka o Kalaehiku e—
The journey upland of Kalaehiku[8]

7. **lehua** "The flower of the 'ōhi'a tree (*Metrosideros macropus, M. collina*). . . . The *lehua* is the flower of the island of Hawai'i . . . famous in song and tale. *Fig.*, a warrior, beloved friend or relative, sweetheart, expert" (PED). In addition, the *lehua* is a furry red flower, somewhat akin to a powderpuff, whose stamens fall off if shaken roughly, and it is often a female genital symbol in sexual allusions. Mentioned in the chant *Pūnana ka Manu* in honor of Kamehameha I. (Sahlins 1985:16)

8. *Kalaehiku* Lit., the seventh peninsula. Not found in PN, PSIC, or on Bier's 1976 map.

Ka loa o ke kanaka e hele ana
(5) The long path that people journey upon

Make i ka ʻōpā maloʻeloʻe
Weary and aching with stiffness.

12 Pele answered him from within the house. "Indeed, you are tired and stiff. You have four feet, your body is hairy, and your ears are long."

13 Hiʻiaka said to Pele, "He says the fish of Puna has come from the sea."

14 "You contradict yourself. There are no people of Puna. If this man of Puna sat down, 'sweet potato sprouts would grow from him.'"[9]

15 Kamapuaʻa said to his grandparents, "Perhaps I in my true form have been seen by Pele folks. You said I would be concealed by you. Here is the opposite! I am very ashamed at my having been reviled for my hairy body."

16 Kūliaikekaua said, "You must say that you have traveled here from the seaside of Puna."

17 *Mai Punaloa au i hele mai nei*
From Punaloa[10] have I traveled here

A ʻike mai nei hoʻi au i nā wāhine ʻeli nomi
And I now see the women who dig for *noni*[11]

Waʻu nomi, kuʻi nomi
Who grate *noni*, pound *noni*

Kāwī nomi, ʻuwī noni, kākua noni
Squeeze *noni*, wring *noni*, bind *noni*

ʻO ke kila i kukiʻi
(5) It is the strong one who binds[12]

I Koʻokoʻolau i Nānāwale.
At Koʻokoʻolau,[13] at Nānāwale.[14]

18 Pele emerged, looked at Kamapuaʻa, and called out, "Where are you from, O hairy man who has journeyed here, trespassing upon our sacred mountain?

9. *a ulu hāwaʻewaʻe akula* Pele says this because the sweet potato is a body form of Kamapuaʻa, making this a derisive allusion to Kamapuaʻa.

10. *Punaloa* Lit., long Puna. This seems to be another name for Puna, a district in Hawaiʻi where Kīlauea is situated. Not found in PN, PSIC, or on Bier's 1976 map.

11. *noni* "The Indian mulberry (*Morinda citrifolia*), a small tree or shrub . . . [with] pale-yellow unpleasant-tasting fruits. Formerly Hawaiians obtained dyes and medicine from many parts of the tree" (PED). "The noni is the plant from which red dye is extracted; the allusion therefore is to Pele's red eyes, and the goddess promptly resents the implication" (Beckwith 1919:326). The rank odor of the fruit tends to cling to those who work with it, hence a further insult. Note that in part of the chant, *noni* is called *nomi*, which is probably a different dialect, but perhaps was merely a misprint.

12. The actual term is *kukiʻi*, which is not listed in PED or LAD. I assume from the context that it means "to bind" (*nakiʻi*).

13. *Koʻokoʻolau* "Hill (also called Puʻukoʻokoʻolau), Mauna Kea qd.; land section, Puna; crater, Kīlauea qd., Hawaiʻi, named for the plant (*Bidens* spp.) used by Hawaiians for tea" (PN).

14. *Nānāwale* "Subdivision near Pāhoa. . . . Unsuccessful fishermen would say that their canoe landed at Nānāwale (*Lit.,* just look around)" (PN).

E noho nō ʻoe a make
"If you stay you will die

A e hele nō a e make
If you go you shall die."[15]

19   Kūliaikekaua conversed with her, gesturing to the seashore of Puna, to the path that Pele often frequented.

20   "Makaliʻi[16] is the bitter leaf, the food of Puna. The smoke has passed to the uplands of Kapapala.

21   "Hilo of the heavy rain. At Hilo we two slept together, O Pele, 'stringing the *lehua* blossoms of Hopoe.'[17] You strung it and I wore the *lei*."

22   Then Pele answered him, "Perhaps when you look, [you'll see] a pig here below. Then you string a *lei* for yourself, O pig, because I have just traveled from the seashore of Puna. There are no people. Should the people of Puna perhaps settle there, and the winter rains come down, then sweet potato sprouts will grow. You are just lying."

23   One of Pele's younger sisters, that is, Hiʻiakawā-wāhilani, said, "O Pele, the touch of your *kapu* skin will free him for us, a *kāne* for the beautiful young women."

24   Pele said, "Don't you be stubborn, O younger sisters. Your 'hidden places' will soon be molested by that pig. I called out to him there. He didn't answer as a man, he answered as a pig. In my travels I heard the composition of his name chant by his grandmother, and this is it":

25   *ʻO ʻoe ia e Haunuʻu,*
You are the one, O Haunuʻu

E Haulani, e Haʻalokuloku
O Haulani, O Haʻalokuloku

15. This is a standard *ʻanāʻanā* curse which dooms the victim to certain death through the power of the spoken word (Elbert and Mahoe 1970:19). Not found in ON.

16. *makaliʻi* "Tiny, very small, fine, wee . . . fig., anything wee, tiny" (PED). Lines similar to paragraphs 19 and 20 are found in chant form in For. Col. 5:334–35.

17. *e kui ana i ka lehua o Hōpoe* An allusion to making love. The *lehua* blossom is the female. In stringing the *lei*, a needle, always a male symbol, pierces the flower, a female, and the union is completed with the completion of the *lei*. Hence the *lei* is a symbol of love, sexual as well as platonic. Hōpoe was the favorite of Hiʻiaka-i-ka-poli-o-Pele and taught her how to dance. *Hōpoe* literally means "fully developed, as a *lehua* flower" (PED 384). Not found in ON.

Ka Manō, e ka iʻa nui
The shark, the big fish

E Uʻi, e Uilani
O Uʻi, O Uilani.

26 Kamapuaʻa did not reply. Therefore, the
younger sisters of Pele said, "Indeed, there perhaps is a man. Who then is lying, stubbornly
insisting it is a pig?"

27 Pele said to them, "I shall call out again."

28 At this time Kamapuaʻa turned and said to his
grandparents, "I thought I could be hidden by
your powers. Now I find it is just the opposite."

29 Pele chanted again:
ʻO ʻoe ia e ka puaʻa Hiwa
You are the one, O dark pig

A ʻo ka Hiwa nui alo ʻeleʻele,
O the great dark one, black-faced

A ʻo Kananakea,
O the pale thin one

A ʻo Haheikea,
O the white pig, with a spotted shoulder

A ʻo Ke Aloalokea,
(5)　　 O the white-faced one

A ʻo Kaʻehu Kalanuhe,
O the *kalanuhe* reddish one

A ʻo Kaʻehu Kalawela,
O the *kalawela* reddish one

A ʻo ke ā iki
O the small jaw

A ʻo ke ā nui,
O the large jaw

A ʻo ke ā poko,
(10)　 O the short jaw

A ‘o ke ā loa,
O the long jaw

‘Oi hele ma ke ‘ekuna,
Rooting as he wanders

A ‘o Haunu‘u,
O Haunu‘u

A ‘o Haulani, a ‘o Ha‘alokuloku,
O Haulani, O Ha‘alokuloku

A ‘o ka manō ka i‘a nui,
(15)   O shark, the great fish

A ‘o U‘i, a ‘O Uilani.
O handsome youth, O restless one.

30 The pig squirmed, his walking became unsteady,
and Kamapua‘a bellowed out.

It is not finished.

PELE REVILES KAMAPUA'A

ISSUE 12

1 Kamapuaʻa slapped his grandfathers [because of the shame he had endured]. This one cast them away to the peninsula of Kalāʻau.[1] The froth of the sea, that was their food. Only some of his grandfathers remained, that is, Kūliaikekaua and ʻAweʻaweikealoha.

2 Pele said,

ʻO Kamapuaʻa nō ʻoe
You indeed are Kamapuaʻa,

ʻO ka ʻelemu papalahe,
Of the soft[2] buttocks,

ʻO ka ihu i hou ʻia i ka ʻaha,
Of the nose pierced with the *ʻaha* cord,

ʻO ka huelo i pili i ka ʻelemu,
Of the tail that clings to the buttocks,

[5] *ʻO ka maʻi i pili i ka ʻōpū,*
Of the genitals that cling to the stomach,

Me ko ihu hoʻi, e Kamapuaʻa, ʻo ihu ʻekuʻeku!
And your nose, O Kamapuaʻa, a nose that roots [in the earth]!

Me ko pāpālina hoʻi, e Kamapuaʻa, ʻo Pāpālina hole maka!
And your cheeks, O Kamapuaʻa, cheeks that are scraped raw!

Me ko kuʻi hoʻi, e Kamapuaʻa, ʻo kuʻi lenalena!
And your tusks, O Kamapuaʻa, yellow tusks!

Me ko lae hoʻi, e Kamapuaʻa, ʻo lae kahanahana!
And your forehead, O Kamapuaʻa, a forehead marked with a line![3]

Me ko poʻo hoʻi, e Kamapuaʻa, ʻo poʻo lolea!
[10] And your head, O Kamapuaʻa, a skinned head!

1. *Kalāʻau* Lit., the club. There is no such place name listed in PN or PSIC for the island of Hawaiʻi. It may refer to Kalaeokalāʻau, *lit.*, the peninsula of the club, of a point, southwest tip of Molokaʻi, named for the club of Palila (PN).

2. The actual term is *papalahe*, which is not in PED or LAD. Presumably, it is a form of *palahē*, "fragile, easily torn" (PED), or "so soft as to flow; flowing soft and slimy, as mucous from the nose" (LAD). Alternatively, it may be two words, *papa*, flat, and *lahe*, "rare variety of *nahe*, soft" (PED).

3. The term *kahanahana* is not listed in PED or LAD. Presumably, it is a form of *kahana*, "cutting, drawing of a line" (PED).

*Me ko maka hoʻi, e Kamapuaʻa, ʻo maka
   ʻalaʻalawa!*
And your eyes, O Kamapuaʻa, shifty,
   glancing eyes!

*Me ko ʻauwae hoʻi, e Kamapuaʻa, ʻo ʻauwae
   lewa!*
And your jaw, O Kamapuaʻa, a dangling
   jaw!

*Me ko umauma, e Kamapuaʻa, ua umauma
   lahalaha!*
And your chest, O Kamapuaʻa, a broad
   chest!

*Me ko ʻōpū hoʻi, i ʻai ai i ke kapu moa a
   ʻOlopana*
And your stomach that has eaten the sacred
   chicken of ʻOlopana,

[15] *Me ko lae hoʻi, e Kamapuaʻa, ʻo lae
   kahanahana!*
And your forehead, O Kamapuaʻa,
   a forehead marked with lines!

ʻO ʻōpū ʻohua!
A swollen stomach!

Me ko maʻi hoʻi, e Kamapuaʻa, ʻo haʻakolū!
And your genitals, O Kamapuaʻa, only for
   screwing![4]

Me ko ʻōpeʻa hoʻi, ʻo huahua kānana!
And your scrotum, overflowing[5] testicles!

Me ko ʻelemu hoʻi, ʻo hamama i luna!
And your buttocks, open wide to the
   air above!

Me ko kuli hoʻi, ʻo haʻakulikuli!
And your knees, that dance so loudly![6]

*Me ko kapuaʻi hoʻi, ʻo Kamapuaʻa,
   ʻo ʻoīlowai!*
And your feet, O Kamapuaʻa, that sprout
   in water![7]

4. The term *haʻakolu* is not listed
in PED or LAD. However, a *haʻa-*,
like the more common *hoʻo-*, is a
causative, and *kolū* is a loan word
from the English word "screw."
Hence, *haʻakolū* could be "to
screw" and may have been slang
terminology of the 1890s. Pele's
reviling chant to Kamapuaʻa fol-
lows a similar pattern in earlier
versions, in naming his body
parts; however, some terminology
is changed, and this version is
much more risqué (For. Col.
5:221; Kahiolo 1978:61).

5. *kānana* Probably a misspelling of *hānana*: "overflowing"
(PED).

6. *haʻakulikuli* Not listed in
PED or LAD, but I interpreted it
as two words, *haʻa*, "to dance,"
and *kulikuli*, "noise, din; noisy,
deafening" (PED).

7. *ʻoīlowai* Does not appear
in PED or LAD as one word;
separately, *ʻoilo* is to sprout,
and *wai* is water.

3   Kamapuaʻa answered Pele, "That's not right, no. I am not the Kama that you know of, O Pele. 'That Kama in the very dainty *lehua* blossoms of Kaliuwaʻa';[8] perhaps that is the Kama you know of, O Pele.

4   "Perhaps it is the Kamapuaʻa of Kamaunuaniho, perhaps the pig-child of Kahikiʻula, perhaps the younger brother of Kekeleiʻaikū. Perhaps he is the Kamapuaʻa you know of. I am not the Kamapuaʻa you know."

5   Pele answered, "It is known, I know, your grandmother composed your name chant":

6   *Hānau aʻe nō a popo*
     Born as a round mass

     Kā ʻolua keiki
     The child of you two

     ʻO Hiwahiwa ʻoe, ʻo Hamohamo
     You are the precious one, the anointed one

     ʻO ka maka o ka ʻōpua
     The favorite of the clouds

     I hānau ʻia i ka uka o Kaliuwaʻa
(5) Born in the uplands of Kaliuwaʻa

     ʻO kou inoa ʻia, e ō mai
     This is your name chant—answer!

7   The head of that pig rolled unsteadily. Pele had really caught him.

8   Pele chanted again:

     Hānau aʻe nō a popo
     Born as a round mass

     Kā ʻolua keiki
     The child of you two

     ʻŌili ana i ka hau anu o ka mauna
     Appearing in the cold dew of the mountain

     ʻO ka ʻili mahana i ka ʻawa o Puna
     The skin is warmed by the *ʻawa*[9] of Puna

8. *O Kama i ka lehua lihilihi lua o Kaliuwaʻa* This seems to be a saying in reference to a special kind of *lehua* that grows in Kaliuwaʻa, the birthplace of Kamapuaʻa. Not found in ON. Notice his underlying shame of his own identity when he comes before Pele.

9. *ʻawa* "The kava (*Piper methysticum*), a shrub . . . the root being the source of a narcotic drink of the same name used in ceremonies" (PED). The *ʻawa* of Puna was considered very special, as it grew up in the trees, where the branches met the main trunk (Emerson 1915:238).

[5]   *'O kou inoa 'ia, e ō mai*
        This is your name chant—answer!

9   This pig didn't answer Pele, but he turned and
    looked above to his little sister, Leialoha, who
    was a sudden rain shower.

10   Pele answered:

        'A'ohe ou o luna,
        You have nothing [no escape] there above,

        'A'ohe ou o lalo nei,
        You have no escape here below,

        'A'ohe nou o kai,
        Not for you is the sea.

        'A'ohe nou o uka,
        Not for you are the uplands.

[5]   *E noho 'oe a e make*
        If you stay you shall die,

        E hele no 'oe a e make
        If you go you shall die.[10]

11 At this time, this pig bent over in front and fell
    down behind. Then he got up and stood up
    straight, and replied:

12   *Mākole, mākole, 'akahi*
        Red-eyed, so red-eyed[11]

        Hele i kai o Pīheka
        Traveling to the seashore of Pīheka[12]

        He aha ka 'ai e 'ai ai?
        What is the food that is eaten?

        He lihilihi pau i ke Akua
        Scraps devoured by the Gods

        He Akua la, he Akua
(5)   A God there, a God

        He Akua nā ali'i o Kona
        The chiefs of Kona are Gods

        A Pa'ia'ia moku o Hilo
        At Pa'ia'ia[13] in the district of Hilo

10. This is a standard curse used
by Pele to make Kama weak. See
also Issue 11, note 15. Not found
in ON.

11. *Mākole, mākole, 'akahi* The
first line of this chant is a taunt,
usually used to tease Pele.

12. *Pīheka Lit.,* "inflamed, of
eyes" (PED). Seems to be a lost
place name; not found in PN,
PSIC, or on Bier's 1976 map.

13. *Pa'ia'ia* Probably a variant
of Pā'ie'ie, "land near Pana'ewa,
Hilo, Hawai'i. *Lit., 'ie'ie* vine
enclosure" (PN).

Hele aku wau o loko o Pana'ewa
I journeyed from within Pana'ewa[14] forest

Nani kūo ka 'ōhi'a
Filled with so many '*ōhi'a*[15] trees

Ikiiki e—
(10) Such stifling heat

Ikiiki e—
Such suffering

Ikiiki hō'ala hiamoe
Discomfort, awakening the sleeper

E ala mai 'oe e moe loa nei
Wake up, you who sleeps so long here

Aia ka lā i o Uli
There is the sun of Uli[16]

Uliuli kai la, e uliuli
(15) The sea there is dark, a very dark blue

*Kau a mākole a wāwahi wa'a i kai o Puna
nei la e—'o Pele*
The red-eyed one appears there breaking
canoes in the sea of Puna—O Pele

Hele a kēlā lihilihi pepeiao, a kēia pepeiao,
Fragments of this and that *pepeiao*[17] pass by,

Ka ua mea maika'i o ka mākole
The fine work of the red-eyed one

'O ua wahine make la 'o Pele.
O that deadly woman, Pele.

13   Pele listened to this chant of Kamapua'a. She
answered, "You think your journey here was
just a woman-seeking trip, but indeed, it shall
be a degrading journey as you will soon find,
O pig."

14   Then Pele urged Lonomakua to stoke the fire.
The fire of the crater erupted violently and
touched the heavens. The fire of Pele came
out until it reached the feet of Kamapua'a.

14. **Pana'ewa** A land division and
forest in Hilo district, Hawai'i,
named for a supernatural *mo'o*
(lizard) of the same name. When
Hi'iaka traveled through this forest, there was a great battle of the
Akua, in which Hi'iaka slew
Pana'ewa (Emerson 1915:30–46).

15. **'ōhi'a** *'ōhia lehua*, "Metrosideros macropus, M. collina" (PED).

16. **Uli** "Name of a goddess
of sorcery, said to have come
from Kahiki" (PED). "The chief
'aumakua of sorcery, but at the
same time having power as a
healer if she would but exercise it."
Prayed to by Hi'iaka in her efforts
to revive Lohi'au from death
(Emerson 1915:144–47).

17. **pepeiao** "Lugs or blocks
inside a canoe hull to which the
'iako, booms . . . are fastened. . . .
Comb cleats for canoe thwarts
or seats" (PED).

15 It was then that Kamapuaʻa began to descend to fight with Pele, but Kūliaikekaua objected, "Don't you go. I'll be in front and you come right behind." Kamapuaʻa agreed.

16 Before Kūliaikekaua descended, he commanded his grandchild saying this, "You watch, and if the fire stands straight up above, then I am not dead. If the smoke blows toward the uplands, I am not dead. If the smoke blows toward the sea, I am not dead. If the smoke blows toward Kona, I am not dead. If the smoke blows toward Hilo, I am not dead. But if the smoke stays right inside the crater, then I am dead, and there is only the road for those who seek life."

17 Then Kūliaikekaua descended to meet Pele. They two began to fight, according to their strengths and capabilities.

18 As Kūliaikekaua was putting out the fire, the burning of the fire became very faint. Pele ran and clung to a space in the rocks, calling out, "Death pierces this one. I thought perhaps this was a war of relatives. Why don't you run off with your adopted child? Why not leave me, your cousin, alone?"

19 Then Kūliaikekaua retreated. He turned and went to the place where Kamapuaʻa was waiting and said, "O Grandchild, my small bit of strength is exhausted. Only you remain."

20 Kamapuaʻa agreed. He looked to his dear sister. The cloud of sudden showers pounded the fires of Pele. Pele looked down at herself and the fires began burning all around her.

21 Then Pele answered, "If you stay, you shall die. If you go, you shall die. I shall start my prayer, and when it flies upward," said Pele, "you will be killed by me. And when my prayer has been said, you will die."

22   Kamapuaʻa called out, "I too shall begin my prayer, and when it is said, you will be killed by me, O Pele. When my prayer flies upward, you will die."

23   This is the prayer that Pele thought of to pray to Kamapuaʻa. It is the same prayer that Pele used when she fought with Punaʻaikoaʻe,[18] but this prayer that Pele had thought of had already been taken by Kamapuaʻa. This is it here below:

24

Mahuka mai Pele i Hawaiʻi
Pele escaped to Hawaiʻi

Hōʻike ai Pele i kona kino
Pele revealed her true form

ʻO ka hekili me ka ʻuwila
The thunder and the lightning

ʻO ke ʻōlaʻi lū honua
The earthquake that shakes the land

Moku ka ʻuwila, ʻowaka ka lani
(5)   The lightning breaks, flashing in the heavens

A kahua i Kawaihae
At the temple platform in Kawaihae[19]

A Pōhakuloa, pau kanikū i ka ʻai ʻia
At Pōhakuloa,[20] the filth was devoured
  in their eating

ʻAi nō i ka hewa
Eating the wrongdoers

ʻAi nō i uka
Eating the upland

ʻAi nō i kai
(10)   Eating the seashore

A lele nō ʻē Nāhoʻaikū
Nāhoʻaikū[21] had already decided

Makaʻu ka lāʻau o uka
The trees of the uplands were afraid

18. *Punaʻaikoaʻe* "A supernatural man with a tropic bird (*koaʻe*) form who lived at Puʻula, Puna, Hawaiʻi, near the place called Koaʻe (which may be named for him). As a tropic bird he often flew to Pali-kapu-o-Kamohaliʻi (sacred cliff of Kamohaliʻi) at Kilauea and hovered there. . . . Later he was Pele's lover" (PED 397).

19. *Kawaihae* Land section on the leeward side of Hawaiʻi between Kohala proper and Kona, near the Mauna Kea Beach Hotel. *Lit.,* the raging water.

20. *Pōhakuloa* "Land division in the saddle between Mauna Kea and Mauna Loa. . . . *Lit.,* long stone" (PN).

21. *Nāhoʻaikū Lit.,* the people who practice *ʻaikū*. Hoʻaikū seems to describe a set of people who "ate contrary to custom" (AP). In particular it is a term applied to Pele's family (Emerson 1915:53).

A ka Pāhoehoe i ʻai ʻia
That they would be devoured by the
   pāhoehoe[22]

A Kihole i ke ala aʻe
At Kihole[23] is the other path

Pau nā wai hoʻolike

(15) The similar waters are destroyed

A Kalae i kau Pulehu
At Kalae[24] is your waterspout

I kukio i manini ʻōwali
In a small pool is the sickly *manini*[25] fish

I Kalaoa, loaʻa ka waha o ka wawae.
At Kalaoa,[26] the mouth of the foot
   was found.[27]

It is not finished.

22. **pāhoehoe** "Smooth, unbroken type of lava" (PED).

23. **Kihole** Seems to be a lost place name; not found in PN, PSIC, or on Bier's 1976 map. Perhaps is Kīhole. *Lit.,* the stripped ti leaf.

24. **Kalae** Ka Lae, "South point, Hawaiʻi, the southernmost point in all the fifty states. . . . *Lit.,* the point" (PN).

25. **manini** "Very common reef surgeon fish (*Acanthurus sandvicensis*), in the adult stage" (PED).

26. **Kalaoa** "Land section, stream, homesteads, Kailua qd., Kona, Hawaiʻi. . . . *Lit.,* the choker (as a stick for catching eels)" (PN).

27. **Ka waha o ka wawae** *Lit.,* the foot of the mouth, which does not make sense.

THE BATTLE

WITH PELE ESCALATES

ISSUE 13

1   *I ka hoʻonuʻu a ke ā hoʻonaenae o Hiʻiaka*
     Eaten with delight by the panting fires of
        Hiʻiaka

     Noho lae i ka makani
(20) Living on the peninsula in the wind

     ʻO ʻeliʻeli kau mai
     May a profound reverence descend upon us

     A ke ā hou i nā puʻu a Pele
     Until the fires burn again in the hills of Pele

     ʻO ʻeliʻeli kau mai
     May a profound reverence descend upon us

     A ka lua o Lanauli
     At the crater of Lanauli[1]

     I kiʻi i Pāhoehoe nei
(25) Fetched here by the Pāhoehoe

     ʻO ʻeliʻeli kau mai
     May a profound reverence descend upon us

     A ka lae Makaʻupili
     At the peninsula of Makaʻupili[2]

     A ka pua i Hanamalo nei
     Upon the flower here at Hanamalo[3]

     ʻO ʻeliʻeli kau mai
     May a profound reverence descend upon us

     A manuka i hope loa nei
(30) Lagging behind to the very last one

     ʻO ʻeliʻeli kau mai
     May a profound reverence descend upon us

     A ke awa pae i kāʻili kiʻi
     At the landing place where the images were
        snatched away

     A ka pali a Mōlīlele[4]
     At the cliff of Mōlīlele

     ʻEliʻeli kau mai
     May a profound reverence descend upon us

     ʻĀmama, ua noa.
(35) The prayer is finished, it is freed.

1. **Lanauli** Seems to be a lost place name; not listed in PN, PSIC, or on Bier's 1976 map. *Lit.,* floating darkness.

2. **Makaʻupili** Another lost place name; not in PN, PSIC, or on Bier's 1976 map. *Lit.,* to fear closeness.

3. **Hanamalo** "Point and cape, Hoʻōpūloa qd., Hawaiʻi. Probably *lit.,* loincloth bay" (PN); 19.10 North, 155 West (PSIC).

4. **Mōlīlele** "Cliff inland of Wai-o-ʻAhukini (South Point), Hawaiʻi. *Lit.,* leaping albatross" (PN).

2 Kamapuaʻa said to Pele, "You will be killed by me. My prayer has already flown, and when my prayer is said, you will die."

3 At this time the fires of Pele began again.

4 Kamapuaʻa turned and looked above to that little sister of his, the sudden rain shower.

5 *Iho mai ana ka ua i lalo nei, e Leialoha*
Let the rain come down here below,
  O Leialoha

E Lei, Leialoha—
Rise, O Leialoha

ʻO ka haka lei o Pāʻoa
The leaping platform of Pāʻoa[5]

ʻO ka haka lei ʻana
The platform from which he arose

ʻO māhele ʻana ka ua
(5)   Dividing the rain

Me ka lā e
From the sun

E iho, e iho mai ana ka ua i lalo nei
Let it come down, let the rain come down
  here below

E ka pūnohu nui o ʻIkuwā
O the great rising mist of ʻIkuwā[6]

Kaʻalewalewa ka ua koko
The low-lying rainbow drifts along

Pō a Kama, a ka pō i hana ai
(10)   Darkness of Kama, the darkness that he
    has created

He ino nou, he paʻa ʻia, ha paʻa ai
A storm made by you—let it be fixed,
  let it be done

E Uli e māhea ke ala
O Uli, make the path hazy.

5. *Pāʻoa* The good friend of Lohiau, Pele's lover, who came to seek the spirit of his dead friend, but instead was taken by Pele as her lover (Emerson 1915:153–54, 215–34).

6. *ʻIkuwā* "Month of the Hawaiian year, named, according to Kepelino, for the roar of surf, thunder, and cloudbursts of this month" (PED). "Ikuwa, corresponding to October, which was the sixth and last month of the season of Kau" (Malo 1951:30).

6 Then the sky was completely filled and the rain began. With one shower the fires of the crater of Kīlauea were put out. Pele and her people ran off. The younger sisters were killed in the destruction. There was no one left to tell the news.

7 Kama called out to his pig-bodies, to the black pig and all the rest. The pigs rooted below in the house of Pele, that is, Halemauliola.[7] When they had finished rooting, there was no house. Pele would have to live off others. The water in the crater receded. That is the nature of the sudden rain shower, it ends quickly.

8 Pele called out to Kamohoaliʻi.[8] Kamohoaliʻi returned from the upper heavens and gave her the coiled roll of hair. Pele opened it and took out the rubbing stick and the fireplow.[9] She gave these to Lonomakua, and the fire was rekindled.

9 Then Kamapuaʻa began to run in his pig form. He sprang forward through the great *lehua* forest, from the mountains to the sea.

10 *Koa* trees grew from the uplands to the sea, also *kukui*, the *kāwaʻu*,[10] the *ʻōhiʻahā*,[11] the *ʻahakea*,[12] the *hao*,[13] the *ʻaiea*,[14] the *olomea*,[15] the *ʻamaʻumaʻu*,[16] the *ʻiʻiʻi*,[17] and the clumps of grass.

11 Pele began to eat. All of these trees were destroyed in the mystical eating by Pele. The upper heavens became very dark with smoke. No one could be seen. Kamapuaʻa could only cling to a clump of *ʻamaʻumaʻu* fern.

12 The fires burned until they found the bristles, that is, the curly pig bristles. The stench of burning pig bristles went out and surrounded the islands.

13 Kekeleiʻaikū smelled the stench of the burning bristles. He bowed his head down, and his tears fell like rain. Then Kekeleiʻaikū hung himself, for the love of his younger brother. His earthly body was left at Puʻu-o-Kapolei while his grandmother cared for it in the house set aside for his bodily remains.

7. *Halemauliola* Lit., house of good health. Said to be a place at Kīlauea volcano, where Pele's *ʻawa* was grown (Emerson 1915:94).

8. *Kamohoaliʻi* "Pele's older and favorite brother" (PED 386). "Most celebrated of these ancestral shark gods is Kamohoaliʻi . . . the shark god to whom all members of the Pele family offer corpses to become sharks" (Beckwith 1970:129).

9. The firemaking implements, the rubbing stick and the fireplow, were used by her uncle Lonomakua to start up the volcanic fires, once they were put out. Because of the sanctity of these implements they were kept in a coiled roll of hair—the hair being one of the most sacred parts of the body. A common metaphor in Polynesia.

10. *kāwaʻu* "A native holly (*Ilex anomala f. sandwicensis*), a rather common shrub or tree" (PED).

11. *ʻōhiʻahā* "Same as *hā*, 7, a native species of *Eugenia*" (PED).

12. *ʻahakea* "Native trees and shrubs (species of *Bobea*)" (PED).

13. *hao* "All native species of a genus of small trees (*Rauvolfia*), related to the *maile* and the *hōlei*" (PED).

14. *ʻaiea* "All species of the endemic Hawaiian genus *Nothocestrum*" (PED).

15. *olomea* "A native shrub or small tree (*Perrottetia sandwicensis*). . . . It is one of the plant forms of . . . Kamapuaʻa" (PED).

16. *ʻamaʻumaʻu* Plural of *ʻamaʻu*: "all species of an endemic genus of ferns (*Sadleria*). . . . Was one of the forms that Kamapuaʻa, the pig god, could take at will" (PED).

17. *ʻiʻiʻi* "Same as *ʻiʻi*: 'short for *hāpuʻu ʻiʻi* . . . ferns; *ʻamaʻu ʻiʻi*, a fern; *pala ʻiʻi*, a taro'" (PED).

14   When Kekelei'aikū died, 'Iouli and 'Iomea became the kings of the island of O'ahu. Kamanumahū[18] and Kapueonuiokona[19] were chiefs below them.

15   Now we shall turn our path back to the main portion of our story.

16   At that time when Kamapua'a was prostrated, he chanted this:

Anianimakani o lalo o Kahiki e—
O Anianimakani[20] below there at Kahiki

'O Hawai'i ka moku
Hawai'i is the island

Pāheahea mai ana kona leo io'u nei
Her voice calls out invitingly to me here

Kāhea aloha o ka ipo e—
The loving call of the sweetheart

'O Anianimakani
(5)   O Anianimakani

'O Kalāmakele, 'o Leleiona, keiki manu o Pū
O Kalāmakele,[21] O Leleiona,[22] bird child of Pū[23]

I ke ala a ke aloha nei la e—
In the path of the loved one here

Aloha wale.
Only love.

17   Then this loving voice traveled to Anianimakani. This was a dream sweetheart[24] of Kamapua'a.

18   This woman cried out, saying, "Perhaps you have indeed been defeated, my love. Therefore I have a little help for you." That one released her wind body, which is called today the Kona wind.[25]

19   The strength of the Kona wind came from the Pillars of Kahiki[26] to Hawai'i. But when it arrived, it was very weak and feeble.

18. *Kamanumahū* Lit., the weak bird; or perhaps Kamanumāhū: *lit.,* the homosexual bird.

19. *Kapueonuiokona* Lit., the large owl of Kona. Note that 'Iouli, 'Iomea, Kamanumahū, and Kapueonuiokona are all birds, as were the chickens eaten by Kamapua'a. The nature of these names foreshadows their later defeat by Kamapua'a.

20. *Anianimakani* Lit., a gently blowing wind; "*fig.,* to travel swiftly" (PED). Here personified as a woman.

21. *Kalāmakele* Lit., the wet day.

22. *Leleiona* Identified here as the "bird child of Pū," but is also the name of a shark and the Milky Way (LAD).

23. *Pū* Lit., large triton conch shell; not significant as a mythological figure. Probably a variant or misspelling of *Pua:* "a Moloka'i sorcery goddess of possession with human and mudhen ('*alae*) forms. . . . Lit., rising (as smoke)" (PED 397).

24. To meet lovers in one's dreams is a common motif in Hawaiian epics.

25. *Kona wind* This wind always blows from the south, usually during the rainy season, replacing the more common prevailing tradewinds.

26. *Nā Kūkulu o Kahiki* Lit., the Pillars of Kahiki. Refers to the pillars which hold up the dome of the sky, through which the sun rises in the east and sets in the west. (Malo 1951:9–11).

20 And this was the Malanai[27] breeze, the one that would push aside the wind of the mountains so that Kama could see clearly and escape. Kama ran to Puna and arrived at Pahuhale,[28] a land there in the uplands, and Kahuwai[29] is the land by the sea.

21 Here was the fire [lava] burning after him, and there were two men also pursuing him. These were Lamakū[30] folks.

22 As Kama descended, he saw some old men, so he changed himself into his human form. Then this one sat down between these old men.

23 Just as he sat down, the Lamakū men appeared and asked the old men, "Hey, did you two not perhaps see a little pig just now?"

24 "We didn't see any little pig. This is our grandchild sitting here."

25 The two Lamakū men stopped and returned to the presence of Pele. Pele asked them, "Where is that little pig?"

26 "We didn't find him. Some old men roasting bananas are what we found, and their grandson. His little stomach was big and distended."

27 Pele said to those two, "Perhaps that wasn't just a small child. Perhaps he was Kamapuaʻa who had changed into his human form. Go again to fetch him and bring him back into my presence."

28 These two set off to go and search again. When they arrived at the place where the old men were sitting, they asked, "Where then is your grandchild?"

29 "He went off to play. Indeed, that is the eternal nature of children. The buttocks can't sit still in one place. He is constantly gallivanting about."

It is not finished.

27. *Malanai* "Name of a gentle breeze" (PED).

28. *Pahuhale* Not in PN, PSIC, or on Bier's 1976 map. May be a misspelling of Pahuhali, a place on Hawaiʻi Island, 19.30 North, 154.57 West (PSIC).

29. *Kahuwai* "Crater near Halepuaʻa, Puna, Hawaiʻi. *Lit.*, water tender" (PN).

30. *Lamakū* Here said to be relatives of Pele, but may also be a "large torch, formerly several feet tall, with the light coming from burning *kukui* nuts strung on a coconut midrib and wrapped in dried ti leaves and placed at the tops of bamboo handles" (PED).

KAMAPUA‘A RACES
WITH KAHAWALI ON
THE HŌLUA SLIDE

ISSUE 14

1. The two Lamakū men looked about in confusion. They had received 'the royal shaft of Kekuaokalani.'[1] 'For him indeed was Ho'oleheleheki'i.'[2]

2. Kamapua'a had traveled on until he saw some people raising pigs. There were nine piglets belonging to their sow.

3. This one arrived there and changed his form into the small body of a scaly little pig, suckling at the breast of the sow.

4. The Lamakū men arrived searching for Kama at the place where the people were feeding pigs and asked, "Have you two perhaps seen a small child with a distended stomach come by your place?"

5. "We didn't see him. We have been searching in the forest for this female pig of ours. There she is there, eating food with her children.

6. "As for the little scaly pig there suckling at the breast of the sow, that's a little pig that has gone astray. He's not one of the piglets of our sow. But the peculiar thing is, the mother pig isn't angry at this pig who has so wrongly intruded.

7. "So we shall raise this little pig until it is big, because pigs are 'postponed bones.'[3] As for the one you two are searching for, we haven't seen him here. Perhaps he has wandered off, as that is the eternal nature of children. Is he a little grandchild of yours?"

8. "He isn't a little grandchild of ours, but he is a child that our female lord, Pele, has commanded us to fetch and bring before her. We thought perhaps we would find him here, but indeed this is not so. Well, we give an affectionate goodbye to you two. Now we shall return without finding him."

9. Then the Lamakū people left and returned directly to Pele. This one then asked, "Where indeed is that child?"

The original publication date for this issue is incorrect; it was the issue for Thursday, July 9, 1891.

1. *Ua loa'a iā lāua ka lā'au a ke ali'i, a Kekuaokalani* Seems to be a variant of *Loa'a i ka lā'au a Kekuaokalani, o Leheleheki'i*. Lit., "You will get Kekuaokalani's club called Leheleheki'i" meaning "you will find nothing but disappointment" (ON 2014). Kekuaokalani was the high-ranking cousin of Liholiho, Kamehameha II, who received the war God when Liholiho inherited the kingdom. Kekuaokalani opposed Liholiho's overthrow of the *kapu* system and so was killed in 1820 (Kamakau 1961:209, 224–28).

2. *nona ho'i o Ho'oleheleheki'i* An old saying meaning that one is only disappointed. *Ho'oleheleheki'i*, "to be disappointed; to be baffled" (LAD). See note 1 above.

3. *iwi pane'e* Refers to the fact that pigs are a good investment, as pork sustains life (*'iwi*).

10 The people answered negatively, "We didn't find a child. We went to the place where the old men were roasting bananas and questioned them about their small grandchild. They told us he had gone off to play."

11 "Therefore we searched further all the way to Kaniahi.[4] We met with two people feeding pigs.

12 "There was one female pig and her eight children, and also one scaly little pig eating at the breast of the mother. We asked, 'Didn't you two perhaps see anyone come here to your place?' They denied that they had seen anyone.

13 "But they were very surprised by the scaly little pig who was eating at the breast of the mother. They said he was a stray pig that had wandered in; it did not belong to them."

14 Pele said to them, "That wasn't just any pig, that was Kamapuaʻa! You two go again to fetch him, and bring him here before me."

15 Indeed, it was the duty of the people to obey the commanding voice. Therefore, they set out once again and traveled to Kaniahiku.[5] The old men said,

16 "Here you are! How quickly you have returned here."

17 "Indeed, what you two have said, O friends, is right. When we two returned we revealed everything to Pele.

18 "And we were sent again to come once more to you here, to fetch that small scaly little pig that feeds at the breast of the female pig.

19 "Where is that little pig that we all saw yesterday?"

20 "Just this morning this little pig was sitting here. And when we went again to see him, there was no little pig. He had vanished."

21 Then the two Lamakū men left this place, and went on to search for the footprints of this mischievous one, until they came to Halekamahina.[6]

4. *Kaniahi* Seems to be a misprint of *Kaniahiku.*

5. *Kaniahiku* "Homesteads, Kalapana qd., Hawaiʻi. *Lit.,* call of Hiku" (PN).

6. *Halekamahina* "Hill and land sections, Makuʻu and Kalapana qds., Puna, Hawaiʻi. *Lit.,* house [of] the moon" (PN). A crater at 19.30 North, 154.52 West (PSIC).

22 However, Kamapuaʻa had already passed through there and was at the foot of a certain hill, which was filled with people dancing the *ʻālaʻapapa, pūniu,* and *ʻokilu* dances.[7] There were a great many kinds of dances in those dark times.

23 He arrived at the place so full of people. While in his human body, he asked them, "What is happening to cause the people to fill up this place at the foot of the hill?"

24 "These are people who have come to see the *hōlua*[8] sledding of our chief, Kahawali.[9] There he is, standing on top of the hill."[10]

25 "It would certainly be better for you folks to give me a *hōlua* sledding board to use, so that I may climb up the hill and go *hōlua* sledding with our chief."

26 "Then do you know how to *hōlua* slide?" said a native.

27 "Yes, that is, if it's the kind done on the back.[11] This is done face down," said Kama.

28 This one climbed up the hill and met with the chief, Kahawali. The chief said, "I am blessed by your becoming my *hōlua* sledding companion."

29 "This is the reason that I have climbed up here, because I saw that you have no companion to *hōlua* slide with."

30 They two decided that this time of day would be the right time for them to go *hōlua* sledding. After this was decided by Kamapuaʻa and the chief, Kamapuaʻa became a person greatly admired by the onlookers, as a beautiful man and as the best of the warriors. And the white loincloth was wrapped[12] around the buttocks of this pig of ours.

It is not finished.

7. *ʻālaʻapapa* "Type of ancient dramatic hula" (PED). See also Emerson 1909:49–56. *Pūniu,* a hula performed with the *pūniu:* "a small knee drum made of coconut shell with fishskin cover, as of *kala*" (PED); *ʻokilu,* probably same as *kilu,* a type of game similar to quoits, in which hula was also performed (PED, *kilu*).

8. *hōlua* "Sled, especially the ancient sled used on grassy slopes" (PED). A sport usually reserved for *Aliʻi.* Hence, Kamapuaʻa reveals his rank when he claims skill at *hōlua.*

9. *Kahawali* A chief made famous in legend. He is usually said to have scorned racing on the *hōlua* slide with Pele, after which she chased him with a lava flow.

10. *puaa* A misprint of *puʻu,* hill.

11. Kamapuaʻa is just bragging here, as *hōlua* sledding was usually done lying face down.

12. The actual term is *moaukea,* which is not defined in either PED or LAD. The meaning is inferred from the context.

PELE CHASES KAMAPUAʻA

INTO THE SEA AND THEN

DECLARES A TRUCE

ISSUE 15

1   As for the people of the gentle sex, they pulled at him, at this one who brought so much delight to the *hōlua* sledding contest. And he was admired profusely by the spectators crowding at the bottom of the hill.

2   At the finish of this one's *hōlua* sledding, Kamapuaʻa knew that the time was soon coming when his body might be taken by his opponent. The woman of the pit was quickly descending upon him. She was very near.

3   When she appeared among the crowd of people, they began to shout loudly.

4   Pele saw her opponent run into the distant forest, so she sent her fire on before her with great force. It chased after this little pig until he was very close to the water's edge. There was no hope for his life.

5   This one leaped into the sea, changing his body into the *humuhumuāpuaʻa*[1] fish. Pele's people, the Hiʻiaka sisters, stood upon the plain. Pele's people had indeed been thwarted.

6   Then Kama's voice was heard ridiculing Pele and her warriors.

7   And Pele said to her younger sisters, "Show 'the hidden places of your bodies,'[2] and our opponent will see them and probably soon return here to land. Then I'll kill him."

8   They fulfilled Pele's command. Then indeed Kama saw 'the hidden places' of Pele's people, that is, the younger sisters, and he spoke revilingly of them.

9   The younger sister answered him, "He is ranting about our 'hidden places'!"

10 Pele told her younger sisters, "Turn your fronts around toward me and I shall try."

11 They turned until Pele had done her part.

1. *humuhumuāpuaʻa* Same as *humuhumu-nukunuku-ā-puaʻa*, "Varieties of humuhumu (*Rhinecanthus aculeatus*). Lit., *humuhumu* with a snout like a pig" (PED).

2. *nā wahi huna o ke kino o lākou* 'The hidden places' is a euphemism for the genitals.

12 Then they all turned to face Kamapua'a. Kama saw them and cursed their bodies, and then 'the house of Kaupō was set afire.'[3]

13 The 'hidden things' couldn't be concealed by putting them in a secret place. Pele said to her younger sisters, "It is only right that we end what we have been doing.

14 "It has already been seen by him, and it is only right that we stop being cruel. Perhaps it would be better to make love."

15 The younger sisters all agreed with soft voices, "It is better to stop. We shall return to the mountain, and we shall call Kamapua'a, our *kāne*, to end the fighting and return with us." Their elder sister agreed and answered,

16 "Indeed, call our *kāne* to return. The fighting is finished."

17 Ko'olauwahineapuakei[4] called out, "Return and live on the land. For you is 'the work that tires the body.'"[5]

18 When the pig heard this, he was comforted by the thought that 'there was water below.'[6]

19 Because of these smooth[7] speeches between the younger sisters of Pele and Kamapua'a, their love for Kamapua'a became very great. They hid themselves in the mountainous land where the snow turns to water. There were no people remaining there; that place was completely desolate of women.

20 Kamapua'a landed upon the shore. There were no people where he landed. It had been his hope to see the women who had called to him.

21 However, now this place was very lonely, and he said to himself, "Where then indeed are the women now?"

3. *ke ā ka hale o Kaupō* Fig., desire was kindled, as the house is symbolic of the human body (Emerson 1909:53). The allusion to Kaupō is obscure but may be a pun, as Kaupō literally means "night descends." Similar in wording to *Ku ke 'ā i ka hale o Kaupō* (the lava is heaped at the house of Kaupō); a saying from the legend of Pāmano [who] shouted this as his uncle Waipū was trying to make him drunk with 'awa before killing him. The saying denotes great distress (ON 1897). Perhaps Kamapua'a found himself in 'great distress' because of his desire.

4. *Ko'olauwahine-a-Puakei* Lit., the windward woman of [the] proud flower.

5. *ka hana iho a luhi ka kino* Fig., lovemaking. Not found in ON.

6. *he wai ko lalo* Fig., lovemaking might ensue. Not found in ON.

7. *kākele* Lit., "to rub with oil," also "to slide, skid, glide, to go rambling at will and hence to do as one pleases" (PED).

22   His grandfather said, "Don't ask about them, and don't wait around with misty eyes or it will be they who come after you. Is this really your idea then?

23   "Ten times have they waited patiently because of your delaying.

24   "It would be better for you folks to be 'tiring' each other out [making love]. They would be 'tired' and you would be 'tired' also. That's what you should do, my grandchild.

25   "It is not for the women to go and fetch the man—that's for us to do, my man. It's like when we two faced the great sea and the tossing of the waves of the ocean, the dark sea, the deep sea, and also the 'purplish-blue sea of Kāne.'[8] Indeed, that was nothing compared to the enticement from within.[9]

26   "Therefore, it would be better for us to trudge along until we glimpse the seashore of Punahoa.

27   "Our staying at this place, a coastline with no people, would be useless. And how then shall we get something to eat? Our insides are trembling [from lack of food]. 'The eyes can brighten again'[10] at the place where the sweetheart lives. For indeed, 'it is the 'inalua vine that is already in the mouth.'[11]

28   "Therefore, resting here is a mistake, my grandchild. And if this one should give you bad advice, it would be a very great mistake. It's better to travel now."

29   Kamapua'a replied, "It would be better for you to hide in my 'hidden place' and completely disappear. I shall be very embarrassed. When Pele and her younger sisters see my 'hidden place,' indeed I shall conceal myself in your 'hidden place' until I vanish!"

30   "But it cannot be concealed from Pele, because Pele has many body forms just as you have many body forms."

8. *kai popolohua hoʻi a Kāne* A famous and poetic epithet common in chants; refers to the deep, and hence dark, ocean (PED, *popolohua*).

9. *Fig.,* facing huge seas is nothing compared to the raging of desire.

10. *polapola aku nā maka* "Bright, as the face of one recovered from sickness" (LAD). *Fig.,* one can be refreshed. Not found in ON.

11. *O nā ʻinalua iho la nō ia i ka nuku* ʻInalua, a kind of vine used for catching fish (PED). *Fig.,* the sweetheart (fish) has already been caught and awaits you. Not found in ON.

31   Kūliaikekaua called upon some of his relatives
      to take away the ugly pig body of Kamapuaʻa,
      and instead release upon him a beautiful young
      body, the body of a handsome man.

32   When Kūliaikekaua looked at his grandchild,
      'indeed the birds went and ate above'[12] at the
      appearance of this handsome man.

33   Kamapuaʻa said, "You should look carefully for
      any flaws or defects upon my body." Kūliaike-
      kaua said, "There is not a flaw upon any part of
      your body." And this is your author's expression
      of affection, in the words of the name chants
      of the chiefs; this is it here below:

34   *ʻAʻohe puʻu, ʻaʻohe keʻe*
      No defects, no flaws

      ʻAʻohe kaulana ʻailolo
      The skilled one needs no fame

      Ua kaʻa ʻia e Hakaioʻe
      Rolled over [beautified] by Hakaioʻe[13]

      E ka māmā holo honua
      By the precious quick one

      Ke kū o ke kanaka maikaʻi.
(5)   The handsome man appears.

35   Because the smoke would take and capture this
      pig of ours, because of this, they two began to
      travel in human form.

36   And there indeed were Pele and her younger
      sisters, returning to their home. Here then was
      Kamapuaʻa following after.

      It is not finished.

12. *Ua hele nō hoʻi a ʻai ka manu i luna* ʻAi, to eat, can also be *ai*, to have sexual relations, as glottals were omitted by Hawaiian-language newspapers in 1891. Hence, the saying might be 'indeed the birds went and made love above.' Also, *A ʻai ka manu i luna* (the birds feed above); an attractive person is compared to a flower-laden tree that attracts birds (ON 3).

13. *Hakaioʻe* Probably the same as Hakaio. *Ua kaʻa ʻia e Hakaio* (rolled over by Hakaio); said of a woman with a beautiful figure. Hakaio was the name of a super-natural tapa beater that rolled itself over the legendary heroine Keamalu to beautify her figure after her bath (ON 2796).

KAMAPUA'A WINS AFTER ALL

ISSUE 16

1   When Pele and her sisters arrived in the crater below and entered their house, Kamapuaʻa was standing above at Akanikōlea.

2   The younger sisters of Pele cried out with love upon seeing him there, but Pele answered them, "Don't cry—one of you go outside. Perhaps our *kāne* has arrived up there at Akanikōlea."

3   The younger sisters of Pele said, "There is our *kāne* standing above at Akanikōlea.

4   "This man is certainly quick. When we left, he had not yet landed upon the shore. Perhaps he is still in the sea, just dillydallying.

5   "Go now and make certain." Then some of Pele's younger sisters emerged from the house, that is, the woman of the *Pua-hāʻenaena* flower and the woman who lives on the coasts.[1]

6   When they two emerged and looked up at Akanikōlea, they quickly noticed this *kāne* of theirs standing above at Akanikōlea.

7   They shouted aloud with happiness, "This *kāne* of ours is standing right here."

8   Pele said, "Perhaps you should call out to our *kāne* and ask him to return. Here is the house, the fish and the *poi,* and everything else.

9   "And here also are the backside relations of the house" [as is often said of in-laws].[2]

10   "Therefore, you should call out to the love that will 'so neatly nail our bones.'[3] He has finished his dillydallying and now it's time for us to delay.

1. Poetic references to Pele's sisters, Hiʻiaka-ikapuahāʻenaʻena and Hiʻiaka-noholae. See Issue 10, notes 34, 39.

2. *he pili pāpākole* (a backside relationship); a rude reference to in-laws, used only in anger (ON 895). Used here to refer to Pele's sisters, as Pele is still irritated with them for being too eager for Kamapuaʻa.

3. *kakia i ka ʻiwi a kakou* Similar to *Kākia kui nao a ke akamai* (the nailing down of a screw by an expert); a boast of skill in securing something and holding on to it. This saying is taken from an old love song in which the singer claims that the love of her sweetheart is securely nailed down (ON 1418).

11   "It is right that he should become tired from waiting. It is a desired prerequisite from the time of the ancestors until now." Pele called out to her 'multitudinous *Akua* of the night,'[4] and this is it here below:

12

> *'O Nāhoʻaikū kāne*
> O *kapu*-breaking[5] male Gods
>
> *'O Nāhoʻaikū wahine*
> O *kapu*-breaking female Gods
>
> *'O ka maka o ke ahi*
> O the eye of the fire
>
> *'O ka ʻula o ke ahi*
> O the redness of the fire
>
> *E lawe aku i kuʻu kino ʻino*
(5)   Take away my ugly body
>
> *A kau i ka haka i Kailua*
> And place it on the platform in Kailua
>
> *A ʻo kuʻu kino maikaʻi a e kuʻu mai.*
> As for my beautiful body, release it
>   upon me.

13   Pele's fine and beautiful body was then released upon her.

14   At this time, Kamapuaʻa prepared himself to descend into the crater, but his grandfather stopped to instruct him on the things that he ought to do.

15   "When you descend below and mingle with Pele folks, and the young beautiful women come to fetch you, don't accept any of them, lest you will soon die. You must refuse, saying, 'I have no desire for any of you; I desire another woman. I shall choose from among you, when "my desire arises."'"[6]

4. *kini akua o ka pō* A standard phrase used in prayers to include all the Gods, so as not to offend any. Gods of the night were called upon for sorcery. See PED, *kini akua.*

5. *Nāhoʻaikū* The name of Pele's family. See Issue 12, note 20.

6. *kū i koʻu ʻiʻini* Lit., when my desire appears or arises. *Kū* has a double meaning, "erect" as well as "arise."

16   The younger sisters of Pele said, "You are young and handsome, and we are all young and beautiful women. And this is the time for all of us to join bodies, 'to quench the thirst in lovemaking.'[7] When we have done this fifty times, then 'the boundaries of the water's surface will be broken.'"[8]

17   Kamapua'a refused them. "I have no desire for any of you. As for judging which type of woman is most beautiful, it is for the man to choose what is delicious. He is the one who eats[9] and relishes the food. Therefore, I shall mingle among you and search for my love."

18   Pele once again changed from her beautiful body and took on her ugly body. She sat in the fireplace with a fine patterned mat over her shoulders.

19   The grandfather of Kamapua'a had continually instructed him that "the old woman sitting in the fireplace with a fine patterned mat will indeed be Pele. You should go and meet with her and share your love between the two of you.

20   "And she will say to you, 'What then is wrong? My sacred skin has touched you, O *kāne*, and this body has freed you from *kapu*. I am releasing you. You may now go and join bodies with my younger sisters. You are a handsome man and they are such beautiful women. Those are the companions that befit 'the mounting of Waialoha.'[10] The hard one needs the hard one for the excitement. 'There is no delaying the surging of the large seas.'[11]

21   "Therefore, how are you, O Kamapua'a, in the 'hastening of the seaspray'?"[12]

7. *e kani pono auane'i me ka naue* *Naue,* frequently used in genital chants, means "to tremble, vibrate," and is a euphemism for lovemaking.

8. *pau ka palena 'iliwai* According to Larry Kimura, a professor of Hawaiian language at the University of Hawai'i, Hilo, this phrase means "has reached their limit and even gone beyond their limitations." The phrase is also found in "'Oni a ka Moku," a song about a steamship with sexual double meanings. Not found in ON.

9. *'ai* To eat; a pun on *ai*, "to have sexual relations" (PED).

10. *ke kau ana i Waialoha* *Waialoha* being 'the waters [of] love' or 'the beloved water'; also the name of a waterfall on Kaua'i, 21.10 North, 159.40 West (PSIC). Similar to *Oki kilohana ka pali o Waialoha* (straight and tall is the cliff of Waialoha); said in admiration of a tall, well-formed person (ON 2465). Also see *Ho'o-kāhi no kaunu like ana i Waialoha* (together there will be friendliness at Waialoha); when mentioned in poetry, it refers to love and friendliness (ON 1075).

11. *'a'ohe ka'uka'u la o ka helena a ke kai nui* "The surging of the sea" is as the surging of one's emotions, an allusion to sexual relations. Not found in ON.

12. *ho'olale a ke ehukai* In the *mele ma'i* "Pūnana ka manu," *ho'olale* is used as a veiled reference to ejaculation, and in this case 'seaspray' is a euphemism for semen.

22 Kama answered. "The sisters will come afterward. First we two shall 'release the canoes upon the ground.'"[13]

23 Pele replied, "Perhaps you should know, O *kāne,* 'Waihānau has not the slightest interest remaining.'[14] The body moves slowly. The days of womanhood have passed on. These are the days of old age.[15] You should go down to that other side.

24 "This is what I am saying to you, my love. You should 'make love' [*naue*] with my younger sisters in order 'to hasten the food of the beauties.'[16] But it is up to you, O companion."

25 Kamapuaʻa said, "This body didn't swim across the great sea for them, but for you alone, and these are 'dead bones' after you are done with them, O *wahine.*"

26 Then Pele knew, 'the prow of Kama's ship'[17] would not veer to the left [south] but would point due right [north].[18]

27 It was just like the pointing of the star Kau-ʻōpae,[19] the canoe-steering star of the people.

28 Pele said, "If that's how it is, I shall go to bathe my body in the water, and put on my clothes so that I look a bit better."

29 Kamapuaʻa agreed with this flattery of Pele's, and she went off directly to a place where she could bathe.

30 This one transformed her ugly features and took on a beautiful woman's body and went before Kamapuaʻa and said, "Let us return to the house where it is secluded."

31 Kama refused, saying, "I have no desire for the inside of the house. Out here the beauty is very fine indeed."

13. *e kuʻu ai nā waʻa i ka lepo* Since canoes are symbolic of the human body, to release the canoe is to make love. Perhaps similar to *pae mai la ka waʻa i ka ʻāina* (the canoe has come ashore); hunger is satisfied (ON 2566).

14. *aʻohe wahi lihi i koe o Waihānau* Waihānau literally means "birth waters," signifying that Pele is beyond childbearing age, or refers to the waters of the birth canal having "dried up," a condition common to older women. Not found in ON.

15. The term used is *kanikoʻo,* meaning "aged, so old that one walks with a cane (a favorite metaphor). *Lit.,* sounding cane" (PED).

16. *i hoʻolale aku nā ʻai a ka uʻi* If *ʻai* were *ai,* without the glottal, this saying would be 'the sexual relations of youth are exciting.' Similar to *Hoʻolale i ka ʻai a ka uʻi* (show what youth can do); let the youth show us what he can do (ON 1093).

17. *ka ʻihu o ko Kamapuaʻa moku* A phallic symbol. For example, see *ʻĀlika,* Elbert and Mahoe 1970:33–34.

18. The image of a ship or canoe coming into harbor is a common sexual allusion, the ship being male and the harbor, female (Elbert and Mahoe 1970: 33–34). Going left (south) or *hema,* is also to go astray, as *hema* means unskilled and incompetent.

19. *Kauʻōpae* "Name for the star Sirius" (PED). *Lit.,* the rising up of the shrimp. In the *mele maʻi* "Ka Ua i Hāmākua," the leaping shrimp is a phallic symbol.

32 Pele replied, "The behavior of this *kāne* is very strange! Indeed, he wishes to 'release our canoes' upon the *'uhaloa* grass."[20] Kamapua'a said,

33 "Indeed, there is *pāhoehoe* lava that is bad for the body. Therefore, let's not wait for even a little now, let's get to work."

34 Therefore, Pele fulfilled the desires of her born lover,[21] Kama.

35 Thereupon they two threw themselves into 'the food of the beauties,' and 'joyous was the bending over of the fisherman, the sea was calm.'[22]

36 They two joined bodies until four days and four nights had passed. Then Pele became truly vexed and annoyed at this piglike behavior of this Kamapua'a. The younger sisters of Pele began to wail at the death [defeat] of their eldest sister.

37 You folks must be a little patient and we shall return tomorrow.

It is not finished.

20. *'uhaloa* *Waltheria americana* (PED). A plant form of Kamapua'a (For. Col. 5:331). A play upon *'ūhāloa, lit.*, long thigh.

21. *ipo hānau* Inferring that from birth they were meant for each other.

22. *le'a ai kūlou a ka lawai'a he mālie* Le'a is also "sexual gratification" (PED), hence, in this interesting metaphor, Kamapua'a is the fisherman. Similar to *Le'a kūlou a ka lawai'a, ua mālie* (the fisherman enjoys bending over his work when all is calm); when the sea is calm and no gales blow, the fisherman can enjoy fishing (ON 1966).

Aole I Pau

KAMAPUAʻA IS

ENRAPTURED BY KAPO

ISSUE 17

1   As for the *Akua* of Pele, they looked about in confusion and wandered around aimlessly outside. Their strength had been taken away by the pig-grandchild of Kamaunuaniho.

2   When it was understood that Pele was going to die, the parents and younger sisters of Pele began to wail. Thereupon, they decided to fetch Lamakū to come before them.

3   They consulted with each other about sending Lamakū to Māui, to where Kapo[1] was living at Wailua,[2] at the Koʻolau cliffs[3] of Māui. Because indeed, Kapo's *maʻi*[4] was the 'flying *maʻi*'[5] referred to in this story of Kamapuaʻa, which could be brought to Hawaiʻi.

4   Then, Kamapuaʻa would be the one to see this large and plump thing passing before his eyes. The idea was decided upon in consultation between the families of Pele and Lamakū.

5   Lamakū was very swift in his journey to Māui, and he met together with Kapo. The native of that place [Kapo] questioned Lamakū.

6   "What is the reason for your swift journey in sailing here?"

7   "I was sent by your lord and older sister.

8   "I have come to fetch your *maʻi* to take it to Hawaiʻi. When Kamapuaʻa sees it, he will be the one to chase it. Indeed, it's your job to fly away, and he will follow after you, leaving Pele behind.

9   "There is no other way for Pele to escape. She will be killed by the excessive rooting of that pig."

10 Kapo replied, "The sea is very good for a rather long journey. Here then—it's not an important matter. Let us eat until we are satisfied. Then you can go and return to Hawaiʻi, and also take with you the gourd containing our possessions."

1. *Kapo* "A sister of Pele and a daughter of Haumea" (PED 388). An *Akua* of *ʻanāʻanā* and *hula,* her particular gift was a flying vagina.

2. *Wailua* refers to Wailua-iki and Wailua-nui, two land divisions in "Nahiku qd., Maui. . . . *Lit.,* two waters" (PN).

3. *Koʻolau* cliffs As the name implies, this is a mountainous land area on the northeastern end of Māui (PN).

4. *maʻi* *Lit.,* genital. I use the Hawaiian term rather than the English translation, as the latter has vulgar connotations not associated with the Hawaiian term.

5. It could be detached from her body and fly through the air as she directed it. It was said to have wings.

11   Lamakū agreed, and after they had finished eat-
     ing, he returned to Hawai'i with his baggage. He
     arrived before his masters who had sent him,
     and they received him with great happiness.

12   But as for the distressing position of Pele, it
     still continued. Then love welled up within
     'Awe'aweikealoha, because it was love that
     was his business.

13   He whispered softly to the younger sisters of
     Pele, "If you speak, Pele's life will be saved."

14   'Awe'aweikealoha was a relative of the grand-
     fathers of Kamapua'a and of Pele, also. That
     was the reason that love welled up within 'Awe-
     'aweikealoha, and his whispering voice gently
     spoke to the Hi'iaka sisters,

15   "You folks should not speak like this of your
     first-born [elder sister]. This is not the correct
     way for bodies to be used. This behavior of the
     pig is very disturbing. If perhaps it were the
     behavior of a human, then we could not
     forgive him when his part was finished."

     [A paragraph seems to be missing here.]

16   Pele and Kamapua'a heard these words of
     the younger sisters of Pele. Kamapua'a said,
     "Indeed, I shall stop, Ka'epulu[6] is the law of
     the chiefs." Pele requested of him, "Let our
     law be for me."

17   Kamapua'a refused. Pele said, "If that's how it
     is to be, then indeed *Kai'okia*[7] shall be my law."

18   Then the sisters went to fetch Pele and return
     her into the house. Pele invited Kamapua'a to
     come into the house to share a meal with them.

6. *Ka'epulu* Lit., the edge of wetness. Although said to be a chief's
law, it is not mentioned in Kamakau's list of chiefly laws (1964: 9,
10, 11, 14, 15, 17). Not recorded in
Kamakau 1961 or 1976, Malo 1898,
or Ii 1959. Not found in ON.

7. *Kai'okia* "Separated by sea,
spared, set apart, separated"
(PED). Said to have been an
ancient law proclaimed by Kānenuiākea after the great flood to
keep the sea apart from the land
(Kamakau 1964:13). Emerson
(1915:40) declares it to be Pele's
law and that "exclusiveness, to live
apart, was the rule of Pele's life."
It seems that by invoking this law
Pele means to forever live apart
from Kamapua'a; however, Pukui
says that "when pronounced over
a person it set him apart as Pele's
exclusively" (ON 1410). Perhaps in
this instance it is the land that is
set apart exclusively for Pele.

19   And Kamapua'a went in, walking in an embar-
      rassed and dejected manner. Kamapua'a
      requested of Pele, "Three districts of Hawai'i
      Island shall belong to you and three districts
      shall belong to me." Pele agreed to the request
      of her *kāne,* that is, Puna, Ka'ū and Kona,[8]
      these districts would belong to Pele, and Hilo,[9]
      Hāmākua,[10] and Kohala would belong to
      Kamapua'a.

20   Kamapua'a said to Pele, "You wait, and if our
      child is born a girl, name her after your side.
      And if, indeed, it is born a boy, choose the
      name after my side."

21   When Pele gave birth, their child was a girl;
      therefore she named her for her side,
      Ka'owakaikalani.[11]

22   As Kama left Pele folks, he then saw this *ma'i*
      dangling before him. He pursued it until he
      arrived at Keahialaka,[12] which is a place. When
      Kama arrived there, this *ma'i* flew until Kūki'i,[13]
      where the land is an open plain. So Kamapua'a
      went there.

23   This *ma'i* flew until Pu'uma'i,[14] which is a
      ravine. When Kamapua'a arrived there, the
      ma'i of Kapo flew out into the deep ocean.
      This one pursued it in his fish body.

24   Two nights and days passed, and this one
      arrived at Māui, at Pueokahi,[15] at Hāna,[16]
      the land about which is said:

25   *Ka ua noenoe kea o Hāna*
      The white misty rain of Hāna

      'O Hāna o ka i'a o Lanakila[17]
      Hāna is the fish of Lanakila

      'O Hāna a ka i'a iki.
      Hāna is the little fish.

8. *Puna, Kā'u, and Kona* These
are the predominantly dry, desert
areas of southern Hawai'i, wherein
lie the active volcanoes Kīlauea,
Mauna Loa, and Hualalai; therefore, Pele chose these as her lands.

9. *Hilo* Village, bay, and district
on the northeast coast of Hawai'i
Island. (PN.)

10. *Hāmākua* "Quadrangle,
district . . . forest reserve, northeast Hawai'i" (PN). Hilo, Hāmākua, and Kohala were the lush
green districts, all located on the
northern half of Hawai'i. These
were to be the lands of Kamapua'a,
as the rain forests were most suitable for his pig nature.

11. *Ka'owakaikalani* Lit., the
lightning flashing in the heavens.

12. *Keahialaka* "Land section
and village, Maku'a qd., Hawai'i,
where Pele dug a crater. . . .
Lit., the fire made by Laka" (PN).

13. *Kūki'i* "Land division,
Maku'u qd., Hawai'i. . . .
Lit., standing image" (PN).

14. *Pu'uma'i* Lit., genital hill.
Not listed in PN or on Bier's 1976
map. However, it is an alternate
name for Kohelepelepe, Koko
Head (PSIC).

15. *Pueokahi* Name of the bay
at Hāna, Maui. *Lit.,* lone owl (PN).

16. *Hāna* "Quadrangle, village,
bay . . . district . . . East Maui" (PN).

17. *Lanakila* Lit., victory; said
to be a place on Māui famous
for its potent 'awa (Kamakau
1976:41). Also, Hāna, Māui, is
often coupled with the saying,
"the yellow leafed 'awa of Lanakila" (Kamakau 1961:385). Similar
to *Ka ua Kūpunikapa o Lanakila*
(the Hold-fast-to-the-clothing rain
of Lanakila); the rain of Lanakila,
Māui, is so cold that it makes one
clutch and hold his clothing close
to his body (ON 1577).

26 Kama searched the Koʻolau area in his pursuit of the *maʻi* of Kapo. Kama arrived at Waialua-nui.[18] This *maʻi* flew to Waialuaiki.[19] Again Kama arrived there. This *maʻi* flew to the roof of the house. When Kama arrived outside of that house of Kapo's, the *maʻi* was hidden inside a bundle. Kama went and stood outside the house, and he peered through the doorway.[20] When Kapo saw the handsome man standing outside, she was filled with joyous affection and called out.

It is not finished.

18. *Waialuanui* A variant of Wailua-nui, a land division at Nāhiku, Maui.

19. *Waialuaiki* A variant of Wailua-iki. See Issue 17, note 2.

20. This is a risqué little joke, because *puka,* hole or doorway, can also be slang terminology for a female *maʻi,* in this case Kapo's.

KAPO'S KĀNE,

PUANUI, IS FURIOUS

ISSUE 18

1 "Perhaps you should come inside the house. Here is the house, a warm place. Come inside, don't be anxious and don't be shy. Everything inside and outside the house is yours."

2 Kamapua'a said, "It's best that the traveler should rest outside the house until 'the puffing for breath is over.' Then he should enter the house." So this pig sat outside and made himself comfortable while Kapo waited and [the sound of] her tapa beater rang out.

3 And when this one's panting for breath was over, Kapo called out again, "Indeed, come inside." Then Kamapua'a went straight into the house and he asked,

4 "Where then are all the people of your place here?"

5 "They are fishing at sea; and where have you come from?"

6 "I have come from right here, and you are the most beautiful woman of these Ko'olau cliffs of Māui."

7 "Yes, perhaps I am lovely to look at above, but here below, 'there is no small edge, there is only a cliff.'"[1]

8 Kamapua'a said, "You are lovely above and lovely below, too." Kamapua'a had just seen that *ma'i* of Kapo that was put away in the bundle. He grabbed it and put it on her body, and they two began to join their bodies.

9 And when a certain person came to the house of Kapo, he saw these two. Immediately he went out in his canoe and sailed to where Puanui,[2] the *kāne* of Kapo, was fishing. Puanui asked that man,

10 "Why does your canoe sail here at noon?"

11 "Indeed, I have sailed here to see you," said the other one.

1. *a'ohe he lihi, he pali wale nō* meaning that her *ma'i* was not attached at that time.

2. *Puanui* Lit., large flower; flower in this case also referring to his member. Husband of Kapo, said to dwell in Wailua, Māui (Ii 1959:18, 47, 150; Emerson 1909:67). Often mentioned with Kalaipahoa are Pua (Puanui) and Kapo, who are also said to be *Akua* of 'anā-'anā of Moloka'i from the time of Kahekili (Kamakau, *Ke Au 'Oko'a*, May 19, July 14, 1870; Malo 1951:116).

12 In this fishing expedition of Puanui, from morning until this time at which they were speaking, there had not been even a little nibble on his hook by the fish. Here indeed was the reason. There was wrongdoing in the house.[3] And Puanui asked this person,

13 "What indeed is your canoe doing in sailing here?"

14 "I shall tell you. I went by your house with the thought that you had already returned. There was Kapo sleeping with another man, and he was a stranger to my eyes. That's the reason that I have sailed here, to reveal this to you."

15 At this time 'the sea of Puanui rose up'[4] and he said, "That indeed was the reason that all my fish got away. There was wrongdoing in the house."

16 Therefore, Puanui turned his canoe toward the shore of the land. The people dipped their strong paddles with great force. He was hot inside when 'the sea ascended to the base of the cliffs.'[5]

17 In no time at all they had landed on the shore. As he left the canoe, he grabbed a paddle and held it tightly in his hands. Then he returned home at a swift pace.

18 The worker [Puanui] arrived, persisting through Wailuanui and Wailuaiki. He continued as time passed and the tide flowed in, while the Ulumano[6] wind blew.

19 When this wealthy person [Puanui] glimpsed this lazy person [Kama] pleasantly absorbed in making love at 'the water surface of Punahoa,'[7] he lifted his paddle up high, and beat it down right upon Kamapuaʻa.

20 When the paddle of Puanui struck down directly upon Kamapuaʻa, that one [Kama] was courteous. 'The child has already flown off, the one who was afraid.'[8]

3. When the men went out fishing, those who stayed at home were to wait quietly, not working and not playing, until the fishermen returned. Should the men have bad luck at sea and return empty-handed, it would be said that some wrong had been committed in the house. (Lecture by Edith Kanakaʻole, July 1978.)

4. *i piʻi aʻe ai ke kai o Puanui* The sea rising represents Puanui's rising anger. Similar to *Piʻi ke kai* (the sea has risen); the temper has risen (ON 2638).

5. *ke piʻi ala ke kai i kumu pali* Fig., Puanui's anger was raging. Not found in ON.

6. *Ulumano* "Name of a violent wind which blows from the south and other quarters, in the night only, on the west side of Hawaiʻi" (LAD). Here used figuratively to describe Puanui's anger. See also *ʻEha ana ʻoe la i ka makani kuʻi o ka Ulumano* (you will be hurt by the pounding of the Ulumano breeze); one is hurt by the sharp words spoken. This is a line from an old chant (ON 270).

7. *ka ʻiliwai o Punahoa* Punahoa, "land sections, Hilo qd., Hawaiʻi. Lit., companion spring" (PN). Since *puna* is an allusion to a woman (see Issue 9, par. 20–24), the water surface seems to be another female metaphor. Similar to *ʻAʻohe lihi ʻike aku i ka nani o Punahoa* (hasn't known the beauty of Punahoa); used when the charms of a person or place are unknown. Punahoa is an unusually attractive place (ON 171).

8. *ua lele mua ka eiki [keiki] ka mea makaʻu* Kama thus warns Puanui that he, Kama, is no longer a timid child but is now a man. Not found in ON.

21 Puanui brought down his paddle for the second time. Kamapuaʻa humped up his back so that Kapo would not be hit, because ʻKapo was left humbled in the water of Niuliʻi.'[9]

22 Kapo cried out with a loud voice, "O Puanui, don't strike this one here! This is not just any man—this is Kamapuaʻa!"

23 Puanui didn't heed this pleading voice of the *wahine,* but struck suddenly with great force upon ʻthe food of the beauty.'[10]

24 Two and three times the voice of Kapo called out to her *kāne.* Kamapuaʻa arose and sat up and conversed with Kapo.

25 "Where should this one go? Above, below, or seaward?" Kapo said, "No, he should not go there."

"Where then should he go?"

26 "Upland in the mountains." Kapo bowed her head. Then the hands of Kamapuaʻa seized Puanui and cast him up into the upland of Wailuaiki.

27 This banana grove[11] flourishing in the uplands of Wailuaiki was called Puanui, and continues to be so called until this very day, after the name of Puanui, the *kāne* of Kapo.

28 Kapo prepared food for them, and they two sat down to this meal. After they had eaten, Kamapuaʻa lived there until two *anahulu* [twenty days] had passed. Then this Kamapuaʻa became aroused with the thought of traveling on, because his love for his elder brother welled up inside of him.

29 He knew that his elder brother had already left his life because indeed he had smelled the stench of Kama's burning bristles.

30 Kapo said, "Don't go. Let you and me stay together, living only for your desire."

9. *Ke waiho pēpē ala o Kapo i ka wai o Niuliʻi* Niuliʻi is a "village, land division and stream, Kohala and Waipiʻo qds., Hawaiʻi. . . . *Lit.,* small coconut" (PN). Coconuts represent the sexual organs of the war *Akua* Kū. Similar to *Pēpē i ka wai o Niuliʻi* (crushed by the water of Niuliʻi); rendered helpless or made humble and obedient (ON 2627).

10. *nā ʻai a ka uʻi* Fig., a lover. See also Issue 16, note 16.

11. Puanui was thus magically changed into a banana grove, a most fitting end for a man with a ʻbig flower,' as the banana is another Hawaiian phallic symbol as the *maʻi* of Kanaloa, *Akua* of the ocean; hence, forbidden as food for women in ancient times (Malo 1951:29; Kameʻeleihiwa 1992:54).

31 "Yes, perhaps it is indeed my true desire, but there must be no entanglement. The love for my elder brother has welled up inside," said Kamapuaʻa.

32 Therefore, Kamapuaʻa continued his conversation, saying, "Tomorrow morning, I shall leave you to live alone in this place of ours."

It is not finished.

Aole I Pau

KAMAPUA'A ABANDONS KAPO

ISSUE 19

1 Then Kapo cried out for the love of her *kāne,* Kamapuaʻa. When they two lay down together on this night, Kapo did not sleep well. She just squirmed back and forth until the dawn arrived.

2 This pig of ours arose first and began to prepare himself. Then Kapo gently asked him to remain, saying, "This night should be for me, for the *wahine.*"

3 Kamapuaʻa said, "Don't delay me. Indeed, I can just see the spirit body of my elder brother. He is damp and cold.

4 "You should wait here, O *wahine,* and if after time has passed, you still love me, your *kāne,* then search until you find me on the island of Oʻahu."

5 "If that is the way it is to be, then your idea is good, O *kāne.* Indeed, the *wahine* shall be the woman who swims out upon the vast sea."

6 The very last *aloha* was shared between them. Then Kamapuaʻa traveled by the Koʻolau cliffs of Māui until he reached Māliko.[1] This one stopped outside of a certain house that was full of people dancing and eating, and playing *noʻa*[2] and *pūhenehene.*[3]

7 The natives called out, "Come inside the house." Kamapuaʻa agreed [without hesitation].

8 "You are a handsome young man. Where have you come from?"

9 "From here in Koʻolau," said Kamapuaʻa.

10 "You are from Māui?" the native asked again.

11 "No, I am from the island of Oʻahu. I have also been sightseeing on Hawaiʻi, and indeed I have seen this land, too. My desire has been satisfied and for this reason I am returning."

12 "Where then is your canoe?"

1. *Māliko* "Gulch and bay, Pāʻia qd., Māui. *Lit.,* budding" (PN).

2. *noʻa* A guessing game played by commoners and chiefs in which a small piece of wood or stone was hidden under one of several piles of tapa. It was accompanied by heavy betting (Malo 1951:225–26).

3. *pūhenehene* A guessing game similar to *noʻa* but only played at night. A pebble was hidden on the person of one of the players as one team was covered by tapa. When the tapa was removed, the other team had to guess upon which person the pebble was hidden. Accompanied by chanting and *hula* (Malo 1951:218). May be also similar to *kilu,* a game played for sexual favors.

13   "I have no canoe. I was just a passenger and I landed at Hāna. Indeed, I have been traveling and sightseeing among these Koʻolau cliffs."

14   A man said, "We heard that should a certain traveling man arrive from Hawaiʻi, similar to you in stature, just as we are seeing him here, that [he would] be marked by Pele."

15   "Perhaps that's what happened," said Kama-puaʻa. "I don't know about these things. I traveled all about Hawaiʻi, and I am now returning to 'the birth sands.'[4]

16   "Let us all come inside and make merry.[5] Then I can rest a bit until 'the shortness of breath is over,' as my journey has been a long one."

17   A woman said to him, "That is not the way we are here. First we eat until satisfied and after-ward we 'make merry,' perhaps 'making merry' inside here with this strong stout one."

18   That woman was very quick in preparing food for him.

19   When everything was ready, this one sat down to eat. Kamapuaʻa did not eat of the pork, because that was his body. This one ate only fish. This one pushed aside the pork *laulau*.[6]

20   This native woman watched him eating fish, and because she saw that the stranger did not eat the pork *laulau,* she said,

21   "You are the most foolish person! [Now I know] you are the one who just abandoned the birth sands. You were the one who walked upon the rough lava. The fine lush oasis amidst the lava flows was left by you 'to release the fishing net.'"[7]

22   Kamapuaʻa said, "I have come. Great indeed is my desire[8] for you, O Chiefess, to drink in your presence, to perhaps eat what you have prepared, and then leave."

4. *ʻke one hānau'* A poetic way of referring to the place where one was born and raised.

5. *leʻaleʻa* This means to make merry, but it also refers to sexual gratification.

6. *laulau* "Package of tī leaves or banana leaves containing pork, beef, salted fish, or taro tops, baked in the ground oven, steamed or broiled" (PED).

7. *e kuʻu ai o ka ʻupena* Perhaps 'to release the net' is similar in a figurative sense to 'release the canoes.' See Issue 16, note 13. Kama as a fisherman is in Issue 16, note 22. Not found in ON.

8. *ʻono* Usually means to crave or relish food or drink. Here it could also mean to desire the body of the chiefess.

23 Kamapua'a continued to eat until 'the thirst of his water gourd was satisfied.'[9] When he had finished eating, this woman said,

24 "Eat until you are satisfied."[10]

25 "I am satisfied. The merrymaking with the natives has been sacrificed. I apologize for the bones[11] before you, O Chiefess, in light of your boundless generosity, for the fine food I have eaten. What then shall I repay you with? Perhaps the only payment are 'the bones' or 'the eyes of the slimy place.'"[12]

26 "There is nothing that should be paid, it is indeed just food. If it is to be like that, then I give my greatest thanks to you."

27 That woman spoke very weakly as she looked at Kamapua'a, such a handsome man. Perhaps she mistakenly thought that this pig desired her.

28 Kamapua'a pleasantly enjoyed their merrymaking at this time. Kamapua'a took the place of honor while they heaped the *no'a* mounds[13] before him. They could not hide their pebble from him, because he had a dual form.[14] They gave him their very greatest admiration.

29 As they urged him to stay and live with them, they provided for him in all the ways that his body desired.

30 They thought that in him they had gained someone very valuable when they went to bet in the *no'a* game. That is what they thought.

31 They thought that he would be useful when traveling around to bet with people who might challenge their candidate in the *no'a* game. These were the thoughts that grew among them at that time. They revealed all their thoughts to him.

9. *a kani ka ia nei muolo wai* A proverb obscure in meaning; not in Judd 1930. Not found in ON. However, gourds sometimes refer to the male genital, as when Captain Cook's men were being tempted by Hawaiian women (Kamakau 1961:95).

10. *E 'ai 'oe a maona* A polite urging required by custom. Even after you have eaten, the host begs you to eat more. Here *'ai* means to eat, but it is also a double entendre on *ai*, to make love.

11. *o nā iwi Fig.*, his life.

12. *'o nā maka o kahi walewale* An obscure saying; not in Judd 1930. Not found in ON.

13. The piles of tapa. See note 2, this issue.

14. *kino pāpālua* May mean dual form, and seems here to also imply *'ike pāpālua*, "to have the gift of second sight" (PED) that probably derives from his *kinolau*, or many body forms.

32 Kamapuaʻa agreed with their ideas, while turn-
    ing away to conceal his true feelings. When they
    weren't looking, this one would become a fish
    in the rock crevices of the sea. On the evening
    of this day, they passed the time away all night.

It is not finished.

KAMAPUAʻA SEEKS THE GHOST

OF KEKELEIʻAIKŪ

ISSUE 20

1　When Kamapuaʻa saw that dawn was beginning to break, he felt the urge to depart with haste. 'The fish of Ukoʻa has fled.'[1]

2　He traveled a long way, and when morning arrived, he was by the sea of Kahului.[2] This one rested at someone's fishing house and was breathing hard outside the door of the house. The people inside exclaimed,

3　"Eh, is there a friend outside the house whose 'feet are shaking like a lover's?'"[3]

4　"Yes, here is a fellow outside crouching in the dewy cold of the early morning."

5　"Come inside, then, O friend." Kamapuaʻa entered, and the *aloha* was shared upon the meeting between the visitor and the natives. They looked at this stranger, and his bearing was that of one who was glorious and beyond compare, the type that is flocked after by youth, and cherished by the gentle sex.

6　They welcomed him and gave him taro and fish and all the things they usually had for breakfast.

7　So this one ate with the natives, and when they were finished eating, they asked him,

8　"From where have you come?"

9　"I have come from the Koʻolau cliffs."

10　"And where is your journey taking you?"

11　"My journey will take me from here until I reach 'the peace of Hauola.'"[4]

12　"Then your journey must be very swift."

13　Right after they had finished eating, this one rose to go.

14　He journeyed from here to the place where he called out to the spirit of the elder brother with this chant:

1. *pupuhi ka iʻa o Ukoʻa* "Ukoʻa is a famous pond in Waialua, Oʻahu. Said of one who takes flight or of something quickly and secretly taken" (ON 2752).

2. *Kahului* "Town . . . port, bay, Māui. Probably *lit.*, 'the winning'" (PN).

3. *haʻalulu kapuaʻi moe ipo* An obscure metaphor, not found in Judd 1930. Perhaps similar to *Halulu me he Kapuaʻi kanaka la ka ua o Hilo* (the rain of Hilo makes a rumbling sound like the treading of feet) (ON 436).

4. *ka laʻi o Hauola* A saying that refers to Lāhainā, Māui (Kamakau 1961:341); *Hauola*, "an ancient surfing area, Lāhainā, Māui. . . . An offshore stone here is believed to have been a woman who was fleeing from her enemies when the gods turned her into stone" (PN). Also see ON 1425.

15   *Hoʻālohaloha mai ana iaʻu kuʻu kaikuaʻana*
Show me your love and compassion,
   O my elder brother

ʻO ka pili manu kahi a kāua e haele pū ai
In the bird-catching places where we two
   have traveled together

I ke kula o Kahinahina
On the plain of Kahinahina[5]

Iā ʻOlohemiki
At ʻOlohemiki[6]

Iā ʻolua la ke kia holomanu
(5)   You two had the bird-snaring rod

Iaʻu la ke kia mahiʻai
I had the farming rod[7]

I na ke aliʻi kaikaina
Made by the younger brother chief

ʻO koko maka pehupehu i ka lā e—
Of the bloody eyes, swollen in the sun

E haʻa—e, haʻa ka iʻa haʻa o Koʻolina—e
Dancing, dancing is the humble fish
   of Koʻolina[8]

ʻO nā paʻakoʻa pani ua o Waikuʻi la
(10)   Of the rain-filled coral beds of Waikuʻi[9]

Iā Waikuʻi hoʻi e—
Yes, at Waikuʻi!

Hoʻohali i kana iʻa ma waho
Bearing his fish outside

Ma loko ka ʻiʻo, ma waho ka iwi
Inside is the flesh, outside are the bones

ʻO ka pipipi kai welawela
O the *pipipi*[10] of the burning sea

ʻO Kahunaikiʻulalena nei la e—
(15)   O this Kahunaikiʻulalena[11]

ʻO kou inoa ia, e ō mai ʻoe!
Here is your name chant—answer!

5. *Kahinahina* Not found in PN, PSIC, or on Bier's 1976 map. May be the lost place name referred to in Issue 2, note 33. Not found in ON. May allude to their boyhood with their mother Hina when they were so poor they chased tiny birds for food.

6. *ʻOlohemiki* Lit., quick *lua* wrestler. Not found in PN, PSIC, or on Bier's 1976 map. An *ʻōlohe* also refers to a very good thief. Not found in ON. Probably refers to his own chicken-stealing episode.

7. *Iā ʻolua la ke kia holomanu. Iaʻu la ke kia mahiʻai* Lines 5 and 6 refer to the early days, when Kahikihonuakele and Kekeleiʻaikū lived by catching birds, until Kamapuaʻa was of an age to help his brothers plant taro, at which he was so proficient. *Kia holomanu* and *Kia mahiʻai* recall Kano and *ʻōʻō,* two phallic symbols.

8. *Koʻolina* A place in Waimānalo, ʻEwa, seaward of Puʻu Kapolei, where his grandmother lived. See Issue 8, note 12. Not found in ON.

9. *Waikuʻi* Seems to be a lost place name; not in PN or SO. Not found in ON. Lit., pounded water.

10. *pipipi* "General name for small mollusks, including *Nerita picea* and *Nerita neglecta*" (PED).

11. *Kahunaikiʻulalena* Lit., the small secret [in the] ʻUlalena rain. ʻUlalena is a reddish-hued rain associated with Kaʻala, Oʻahu (PED). This seems to be a name of Kekeleiʻaikū.

16　The spirit of Kekelei'aikū returned. Kamapua'a urged the spirit of his elder brother from behind,

17　"Return the spirit to Pu'u-o-Kapolei. There indeed should your spirit dwell, at the place where your body has been deposited.

18　"That place where you were in such intense grief that you had hanged yourself for the love of your younger brother. Return there and wait. Dwell there with our grandmothers, Kamaunuaniho and Wahineokama'o."[12]

19　Then Kamapua'a traveled until he reached Hālawa.[13] From there he went on until Moku-'ume'ume.[14] He lived inside of a certain cave, because the day had become evening.

20　And because Kamapua'a lived in that cave, this cave has been called Keanapua'a[15] until these times.

21　On this very evening, some canoes were sailing from the shores of 'Ewa,[16] filled with calabashes of *poi*, cooked pork, uncooked pork, fish, sugarcane, gourds, bananas, and water gourds.

22　There were eight canoes. This food that the people were bringing was food belonging to the kings of O'ahu, that is, 'Iouli and 'Iomea, who had replaced King 'Olopana when he died.

23　The canoes landed at the place where Kamapua'a was staying, because it was low tide. There they would sleep until the high tide arrived at dawn. Then they would sail for Kou,[17] where the kings were living. Kou is called Honolulu in these times.

24　When they had landed, Kamapua'a moved in swiftly and silently in his pig body. Their canoes were covered over, just outside of Keanapua'a.

12. *Wahineokama'o* Lit., women of the green. Said here to be the companion of Kamaunuaniho, but was also the classic companion of Hi'iaka. See Issue 8, note 18.

13. *Hālawa* Ahupua'a between Moanalua and 'Aiea, adjoining the east side of Pearl Harbor, O'ahu (SO map of 'Ewa).

14. *Moku'ume'ume* "Old name for Ford Island, Pearl Harbor, O'ahu. . . . Lit., 'ume game island (famous for this sexual game)" (PN).

15. *Keanapua'a* Lit., "the pig's cave," located on the beach at Hālawa (SO 10), but here said to be on *Moku'ume'ume*.

16. *'Ewa* A major land district of O'ahu, stretching from Hālawa on the east to Honouliuli on the west and encompassing Pearl Harbor (SO map of 'Ewa).

17. *Kou* "Old name, until 1800, for Honolulu Harbor and vicinity, including the area from Nu'uanu Avenue to Alakea Street, and from Hotel Street to the sea" (PN).

25 The canoes of these people had been safely landed, and they prepared a large place to spend the night. They ate until they were satisfied and dropped off to sleep in comfort.

26 That night the pig went up and climbed into the canoes. All the fish, *poi*, and other food of six canoes were eaten by this pig. All that remained was the cooked pig and the raw pig, because this was his body form.

27 Two canoes remained with all of their food, unmolested by Kamapua'a.

28 As for the six canoes, Kamapua'a filled the calabashes with his excrement and the water gourds with his urine.

29 When the people awoke at dawn, with the idea that they would now travel, they smelled the stench of his excrement.

30 One said, "The odor of excrement is very strange. Has one of us done something wrong?"

31 They all denied it, "Nothing wrong has been done by us. Not one of us awoke before the others."

32 Let us be patient and see what appears tomorrow.

It is not finished.

Aole I Pau

KAMAPUA'A PUZZLES 'IOMEA

AND 'IOULI'S PEOPLE

ISSUE 21

1. When they went out upon the canoes, they quickly saw the excrement, the stuff that filled the calabashes, and the urine that filled the water gourds. Everything had been eaten in the six canoes except the pork.

2. There were two other canoes upon which the food had not been molested. They exclaimed, "Kamapuaʻa lives again, and he is the one who has done these strange deeds."

3. "Indeed, the stench of the burned bristles of the pig rose up and filled the islands, and Kamapuaʻa had been killed by Pele. Here then he lives again!"

4. The people on these canoes had a discussion among themselves. As for the six canoes from which the food had been eaten, these canoes were to return to the uplands of ʻEwa, to get more food for them. As for the remaining two canoes, they were to sail on ahead.

5. Those people returned to the uplands of ʻEwa. As for these two canoes, they prepared for their sailing.

6. In these canoes, the people's food was securely placed. As they began to sail, this pig appeared on the sandy peninsula crying out.

7. When the people heard the pig's crying voice behind them, their eyes turned and looked straight up at the cave. This pig was standing right there.

8. They turned back the canoes to go and fetch the pig to load on as cargo. When they landed on the shore, they seized this pig and put him on board the canoe.

9. As they were sailing along, a certain man said, "This is a fat juicy pig and would be delicious flesh for the kings, because this is an Olomea[1] pig. Lightly salt the flesh of this kind of pig and it's really delicious."

1. *Olomea* "Brown, with darker stripes or spots, of pig or dog" (PED).

10   While these people were talking, the eyes of this pig watched them intently.

11   Between these two canoes, there was nothing for these people to eat. As they approached the point of Kepoʻookalā,[2] the pig arose and plopped into the sea. This pig departed in haste and landed on the shore. A fishpond was the place where he landed.

12   Kamapuaʻa began to climb upland of Honouli-uli[3] until he arrived at Honouliuli Pond.[4] This one saw an old woman beginning to gather the ʻohā[5] floating on the water inside of the taro patch.

13   Kamapuaʻa stood on one side of that taro patch, while the old woman was gathering ʻohā floating on the water.

14   When this woman turned, she saw this man standing in the field.

15   The old woman gave her *aloha* to this man standing there. And indeed, Kamapuaʻa gave his *aloha* in the same manner. And he asked, "What are you doing?"

16   "I am gathering a few ʻohā floating on the water, so that I may live. This is a time of famine for the land. What is the alternative?"

17   Then Kamapuaʻa saw a certain taro patch where the taro had grown to maturity. He asked the woman, "What is the reason for gathering this? You should leave this place for another taro patch that is mature."

18   The old woman said, "That mature taro patch belongs to the king. It's not for people like us."

19   Kamapuaʻa said, "Perhaps the people ought to catch this king. It is the people who grow it and cook it, and the king only eats it! I will be the one who will pull the taro for us."

2. *Kepoʻookalā* Lit., the head of the sun. A point on Waipiʻo peninsula in Pearl Harbor, now known as Poʻokalā (SO map of ʻEwa).

3. *Honouliuli* A large *ahupuaʻa* adjoining Pearl Harbor, bounded by Hōʻaeʻae on the east and Nānā-kuli on the west, stretching from Wahiawā to the sea. Includes Puʻu-o-Kapolei (SO map of ʻEwa). *Lit.,* dark bay.

4. *Honouliuli Pond* This may be what is referred to as Kaloʻi, an old taro patch and freshwater spring that is lost today (SO 35).

5. *ʻohā* "Taro growing from the older root, especially from the stalk called *kalo*" (PED).

20 The old woman said, "We shall soon be killed by the king. No sooner would we eat the taro than we should be killed."

21 "Is that so! Perhaps we shall not be killed by the king, but it will be the king who will flee. 'The royal stomach should be a loving stomach.'[6]

22 "Therefore let the two of us return to the open plain, and I shall be the one who will pull lots of taro for us."

23 Kamaunuaniho said, "Indeed, I shall be killed because of your behavior. This old woman has just a few loved ones. This is not the time to become a corpse. Here I am already dead because of the stealing of the king's taro. I shall not see my grandchild because of this sorry business."[7]

24 Kamapua'a pulled up the taro of the king's taro patch with his great strength, from one side to the other, until the wealth of this taro patch was floating on the water.

25 Kamaunuaniho continued to bewail her impending execution by the king. All the taro of this taro patch was gathered together by Kamapua'a, who said to the old woman,

26 "Our taro has been collected. Now it only remains to be placed upon your back to be carried."

27 The old woman said, "I can't carry all the taro. Perhaps we had better carry our taro a little at a time until we are finished."

28 "Perhaps you should try to carry our food at this time." She agreed.

29 When their taro was placed upon the neck of Kamaunuaniho, Kamapua'a called upon his grandfathers—for them to take away the weight of the burden upon his grandmother.

6. *he 'ōpū ali'i ho'i, he 'ōpū aloha* An obscure proverb, but meaning figuratively that the chiefs should share their food; not in Judd 1930. Not found in ON. Note that since there was a famine on the land, it indicated that the new kings had lost divine favor and were no longer *pono*. They were not fulfilling their chiefly responsibilities to make the land fertile and to feed the people. Hence, they deserved to be overthrown. And, as usual Kamapua'a is disdainful of chiefly authority not his own. Note that the sons of 'Olopana were his senior lineage cousins.

7. Note that she does not recognize her grandchild Kamapua'a. Perhaps her eyesight is bad from old age.

30   Kamaunuaniho went on until they arrived at
     the hill of Kapolei, and Kamapuaʻa followed
     right behind.

31   When Wahineokamaʻo saw what Kamaunua-
     niho was carrying, she began to wail at their
     execution by the king.

32   They two lighted the underground oven, and
     they cooked the best of the taro. They did not
     cook most of their taro.

KAMAPUAʻA MEETS
A MOʻO WOMAN AND
DRINKS ʻAWA

ISSUE 22

1. This is the previous section of the story of Kamapua'a from last Monday. [This episode should have been inserted into that portion of the epic presented in Issue 20, because it occurs on Māui, before Kamapua'a returns to O'ahu. Perhaps the original typesetter misplaced a few pages of the handwritten copy as he was working.]

2. Kamapua'a left Kahului, having given his last *aloha* to the natives of the house where he had first visited.

3. Kamapua'a set off for the shore of Wailuku.[1] When he arrived at the sandy point on this side of the Wailuku River, a certain woman called out in greeting.

4. "Come visit in my house and eat, O stranger."

5. Kamapua'a said, "I have eaten my fill at the house I visited in Kahului."

6. The woman said, "That is nothing; come into the house and eat, because evening is near. Eat your fill, then sleep in the house. Here is the house—it is a generous house."

7. Kamapua'a refused, saying, "I have no desire. I shall travel until the night is very dark, only then and there will I sleep."

8. Your author should explain about this woman. The name of this woman was Waihīnanoikapo'ipo'i.[2] This woman was a closely related cousin of Pele.

9. At this time, Waihīnanoikapo'ipo'i knew that this handsome young stranger would not agree to her suggestions.

10. Thereupon, Kamapua'a gave his *aloha* to Waihīnanoikapo'ipo'i and turned to continue on his journey.

11. The name of this place of Wailuku has been called Waihīnano even until these very enlightened times.

1. *Wailuku* "Land division . . . city, point . . . stream, West Maui. . . . *Lit.*, water [of] destruction" (PN).

2. *Waihīnano-i-ka-po'ipo'i Lit.*, the juice of the male pandanus blossom that has been cupped in the hands; name of the chief adviser to King 'Olepau of 'Īao valley (Emerson 1915:74–80). Not found in ON. The male pandanus blossom was sprinkled on the skin of one's lover and used as an aphrodisiac.

12 Kamapuaʻa continued on until he met with a certain woman swimming in a pool of water combing her luxuriant dark hair.³

13 And the voice of that woman called out in greeting to him, "You there! Let's you and I go bathe to remove the grimy sweat of your journey on the long road. I'll be the one to wash the dirt from your back. And indeed, I'll be the one to massage the aching tiredness of your feet.

14 "And when we two have finished bathing, then we can return to my home. There there is taro, fish, water, and everything that you might desire. This day is wasted, because the sun is already beginning to set. Sleep, and when it is morning, travel on. There is another day."

15 Kamapuaʻa said, "I don't have a desire to eat. Nor do I have any desire for the other things which you have mentioned. My love for my elder brother is greater at this time.

16 "I shall continue until the night is very dark, then I shall sleep."

17 "You are exceedingly disobedient, O man. If perhaps you had a human ear, then you would hear [and obey]."⁴

18 Kamapuaʻa said to that woman, "I am not a suitable match for you, because you are a woman of the water. I am a man of the dry land. 'The thrill of love at Waialoha'⁵ is not appropriate; therefore I shall soon say goodbye to you, as I am about to go on."

19 That woman said, "What you have said to me is true, but you and I are also alike in that we have supernatural body forms.

20 "I have a different body form within the water, and so also do you. Indeed you have a supernatural body, O pig-grandchild of Kamaunuaniho."

3. A woman swimming alone in a pool or sitting beside a pool combing her hair is usually indicative of a *moʻowahine*, or lizard-woman, a being that could change shapes as Kamapuaʻa did. *Moʻowahine* liked to kill their lovers when they were finished with them.

4. In the Hawaiian way of thinking, "to hear" is "to obey."

5. *ke kāunu ʻana i Waialoha* Waialoha, *lit.,* beloved waters or water [of] love, is a pun upon the water (*wai*) that is this woman's home and those waters exuded in lovemaking. See Issue 16, note 10. Also *ʻkāunu,* desire, passion. "*Wai o kaunu, lit.,* the water of love—'the warm effects'" (Emerson 1915:108).

21 Kamapuaʻa just turned to go on his way, because the sun was setting.

22 Your author shall [now] reveal the name of this woman. Paukūkalo[6] was her name.

23 And the name of the pool where she was bathing just seaward of Wailuku has been called Paukūkalo until this very day.

24 Kamapuaʻa journeyed until he arrived by the sea of Waiʻehu.[7] He saw a fishing canoe returning to the shore.

25 Indeed that canoe was coming in full of fish. When it landed, these men had to carry it to land. These men lifted their canoe, but it couldn't be brought all the way up, as it was so full of fish.

26 As he had been sitting in a crouching position, Kamapuaʻa stood up. His hands seized the *manu*[8] of the canoe and raised it up, carrying it along with the natives, until the canoe was properly landed at its resting place.

27 A man turned and saw Kamapuaʻa standing behind the canoe. He gave him his *aloha* and asked him,

28 "You are very swift. From where have you come?"

29 "From the Koʻolau area of Māui. I am a visitor."

30 "If it should please you, O visitor, you and I can sleep at my house here."

31 "Is it only you then perhaps who lives here at your house?"

32 "Yes, only me."

33 "Yes, then let you and me sleep here tonight."

34 This native prepared the food, broiling some fish.

6. *Paukūkalo* Lit., a piece of *kalo* (taro). Said to be a place frequented by *moʻo* (lizard gods) (Kamakau 1964:83, 85).

7. *Waiʻehu* "Land division, point, streams, village, beach. . . . Wailuku qd., Maui. Lit., water spray" (PN).

8. *manu* "Ornamental elliptical expansions at the upper ends of the bow and stern endpieces" (PED).

35 When Kamapua'a looked at the wall of the
    house, he saw two 'awa roots hanging there.
    He said to his native friend,

36 "Here then is our food, the 'awa."

37 "You should mash these leaves."

38 "Yes, I shall mash them. I shall be very quick
    at making 'awa for you and me. How many
    māna[9] of 'awa shall we have?

39 "Perhaps then there should be two because
    there are two of us."

40 The native said, "Perhaps you and I won't
    even get 'salted.'[10] Perhaps if we have four 'awa
    māna, then you and I can be properly satisfied."

9. *māna* "A chewed mass, as of *kava* for drinking" (PED).

10. *mikomiko* Lit., lightly salted, a slang term akin to *noenoe*, misty, meaning drunk. The native is hospitable to offer so much.

AFTERWORD

Pīpī holo ka'ao. Minamina kākou e ha'alele ai i kēia pua'a kolohe, akā 'ano kūpono paha e ho'opau ai i kēia 'āpana o ka mo'olelo me nā wāhine kupaia-naha o Māui i ho'oma'ewa kiko'olā 'ia ai e Kamapua'a.

So the story goes. We regret leaving this mischievous pig, but it is perhaps appropriate to end this portion of the epic with Kamapua'a rudely spurning the supernatural women of Māui. The episode illustrates perfectly the pig-man's fickle nature.

The first woman spurned is Waihīnanoikapo'ipo'i, a relative of Pele. In the past, Pele had nearly killed the pig and was famous for having burned his pig bristles. He is wise to be wary of anyone in her family. The second woman is Paukūkalo, a *mo'o*, who chides Kamapua'a for his reluctance to accept her sexual advances, accusing him of being "extremely disobedient" (Issue 22).

Kamapua'a escapes with the excuse of an errand more pressing—he must recapture the spirit of his recently deceased elder brother Kekelei'aikū. He has no time for dalliance, as his brother's spirit must be caught and Kekelei-'aikū restored to life. Such filial devotion. At least it is a plausible excuse for escape. Kamapua'a may well be remembering that *mo'o* women have an unfortunate tendency to kill their human lovers at the end of an affair. His contretemps with Pele had been dangerous enough.

Instead of another love affair, Kamapua'a chooses to "get salted" by drinking *'awa* with one of the "boys," in this instance, a hospitable fisher-man from Wai'ehu. Wai'ehu is the *ahupua'a* adjacent to Waihe'e, birthplace of the ancestors of Kamapua'a. In this way, the first third of the Kamapua'a epic has come full circle, and we are left waiting with baited breath for the next two-thirds of the epic, now in the translation process.

The audience of 1891 was fortunate, as each new installment of the pig's adventures was available on a daily basis. In all, sixty-seven installments of the Kamapua'a epic ran in *Ka Leo o ka Lāhui*, ending on September 28, 1891. Later issues presented the further exploits of Kamapua'a on O'ahu, with Kekelei'aikū raised from the dead; with continued opposition to his royal cousins 'Iomea and 'Iouli, the kings of O'ahu; and with Kū'īlioloa, the man-eating dog *Akua* of Wahiawā. Later, Kamapua'a travels to Kaua'i, meets the ogre Limaloa, seduces chiefly women, and battles with *mo'o* women.

In keeping with Hawaiian convention, the story doesn't end with the telling. Now is the time for the audience to evaluate the interplay of *kaona* in the epic. What are the deeper meanings and lessons to be learned? Is there just one level of *kaona* or are there several?

One striking departure from traditional custom is the number of times women invite Kamapua'a to eat with them. The word *'ai*, meaning to eat, has a double connotation with *ai*, to make love: repeatedly, women want to seduce the virile young hero.

In contrast, the traditional *'Aikapu* religion demanded that men and women eat separately. The *'Aikapu* (literally, sacred eating), which made the preparation and consumption of food a religious rite, was the foremost *kapu* of ancient Hawai'i and the foundation of Hawaiian religion. *'Aikapu* required that men cook all food in separate ovens, one for women's food, another for men's; that men and women eat in separate houses; and that women be forbidden certain foods, including pork, bananas, coconuts, and certain fish, especially red fish (Malo 1951:27–30).

These foods were sexual symbols of powerful male *Akua* (Kame'eleihiwa 1992:34). Any of these foods were considered an appropriate sacrifice to the male *Akua* of the *luakini* temple (For. Col. 6:2–45) and would be defiled if cooked or eaten by women. Women were thought to have had a polluting influence on male sacrifice because women menstruate. It seems that male *Akua* were afraid of female blood. Such fear was fortunate for women, however, because men were by this reckoning sacred, and since most food had a sacred male essence (growing out of the female earth), men were required by the *Akua* to do all the cooking! Also, men were the only appropriate human sacrifice.

The *'Aikapu* is said to have been a law established in the time of Wākea in conjunction with *kapu* nights, when men went to worship the male *Akua* at the temple and were forbidden to sleep with women (Dibble 1843:12–13; Beckwith 1970:296–298). It was a very serious law and ordered all parts of society. Only when Liholiho decided in 1819 to break the *'Aikapu*, when he sat down to eat with the *ali'i* women, was that ancient state religion destroyed (Kamakau 1961:224–225). Yet throughout the Kamapua'a epic, men and women eat together in open violation of the *'Aikapu*.

How could the characters in our epic ignore the most ancient laws and eat with men and women together? Was this a modern invention added to the story in 1891? Was this an ancient symbol of rebellion against the chiefly religion that required separate eating? Did the illicit activity, which everyone knew was a great wrong, punishable by death, add tension and excitement? Or did the *maka'āinana* generally ignore the *'Aikapu* when the chiefs were not present?

Subtle references to *'Aikū* appear throughout the story. The word *'Aikū* literally means "to eat in an improper manner" (LAD), "to take food that is set apart as temporarily or permanently sacred or forbidden to use," and "to act contrary to custom, prescribed rule, or established precedent; to overlook, disregard, or take no notice of a tabu" (AP). It is part of the name given to Kekelei'aikū, the favorite brother of Kamapua'a (Issue 2) and is also used in the name given to Pele's family, Nāho'aikū (Issue 16).

One translation of the name Kekelei'aikū is "pork fat eaten contrary to ceremony or without consecration." *Ali'i Nui* were expressly prohibited from eating unconsecrated pork (Malo 1951:143). Nāho'aikū, on the other hand, might be translated as "the companions who disregard or take no notice of a tabu," a strange appellation for Pele and her family, as they were protected by many severe *kapu* that regulated every approach to the sacred women (Emerson 1915). However, it may have been that the Pele *kapu* were not the same as those practiced by the *Ali'i Nui* who lived under the *'Aikapu.*

Moreover, *'Aikū*, or 'Aitu in Tahiti and Sāmoa (Henry 1985:385, Turner 1984:23), is an old Polynesian word for *Akua.* Perhaps 'Aitu were a class of Gods that formerly required different eating laws.

According to Malo, it was the *Ali'i Nui* who had to follow the *'Aikapu* most strictly. Kamakau agrees, stating that a *Mō'ī* who did not follow the *'Aikapu* had not long to rule. The political power of the *'Aikapu* depended most heavily upon the worship of Kū, or Kūnuiākea, at the *luakini.* He was the *Akua* who demanded human male sacrifice. Kū ruled the land for eight months of the year, while Lono, the *Akua* of peace and fertility, ruled for only four months of the Makahiki festival. Lono abhorred human sacrifice. The worship of Kūnuiākea is said to have begun with the coming of Pa'ao, a *kahuna* from Kahiki, who left after a nasty argument with his older brother Lonopele (Kamakau 1991:5). Pa'ao is also said to have come from the islands of 'Upolu or Vava'u, which were once the names of Taha'a and Borabora (Henry 1985:102).

Borabora is the island Pele came from long ago. Lonomakua is the name of Pele's uncle who teaches her the secret of making fire and is the name of the principal Makahiki image. Lono is also named as one of the ancestors of Kamapua'a, and the common pig, as well as Kamapua'a, is *kinolau*, or a body form of the great *Akua* Lono. During the Makahiki, pork was not eaten, out of respect for Lono.

The *Akua* and ritual brought by Paʻao is remarkably similar to that practiced by the *Kahuna Nui* or high priests of the temple, called Taputapuātea, located on the island of Raʻiātea. Raʻiātea is one day's sail south from Tahaʻa and Borabora. Tahaʻa is actually within the same fringing reef as Raʻiātea. Raʻiātea, too, is only one day's sail from Tahiti and was the religious center of those islands.

Regular offerings at the most sacred temple of Taputapuātea included humans, sharks, turtles, and *ʻulua* (jack crevalle) fish (Henry 1985:124). Similar offerings were given at the temples in Hawaiʻi to Kūnuiākea, Lononuiākea, and Kānenuiākea. Notice the *ākea* suffix attached to the great *Akua* names, similar to Wākea, the name of the Hawaiian sky-father who procreates with his sister Papahānaumoku, the earth-mother, to produce the islands of Hawaiʻi. Hawaiʻi, or in its older Polynesian form, Havaiki, is the original name of the island of Raʻiātea.

Is it possible that Pele and Kamapuaʻa of the ʻAitu family represented older *Akua* that came with earlier migrations who did not follow the *ʻAikapu?* It may have been that *ʻAikū* connoted a set of *Akua,* perhaps of the family of Lono, that were demoted in the Hawaiian pantheon by the emergence of a new lineage of chiefs and their war *Akua* Kū, but were never forgotten by those Hawaiians, now commoners, who were related to and worshipers of Pele and Kamapuaʻa.

Perhaps their *mana,* or spiritual power, was eclipsed by the newer Kū *Akua* brought by Paʻao, which demanded male sacrifice, as well as a strict adherence to *ʻAikapu* and the separate eating of men and women. Note that although Kū's power surpassed Lono's, as indicated by the greater length of time devoted to his worship, when Pele and Kamapuaʻa pray to their *Akua* for success in *ʻanāʻanā* and in war, they never pray to Kūkāʻilimoku or Kūnuiākea or any of the *luakini* ritual *Akua.* In later times, Kū was the very *Akua* most closely associated with *ʻanāʻanā* and war (Malo 1951:82, 159–160).

Another *kaona* in the epic not readily apparent to the general reader of today is the familial relationship between Pele and Kamapuaʻa. Only those few Hawaiians of 1891 who still worshiped Pele as their *ʻAumakua,* or family guardian, would have known her genealogy, but the more traditional Hawaiian audience of 1791 would have been fully aware that Pele and Kamapuaʻa were cousins. The mother of Pele is Haumea, the female *Akua* of Borabora widely worshiped in Kahiki. The Kamapuaʻa epic begins with Kananananuiʻaimoku of Waiʻehu, Māui, and Haumealani (heavenly Haumea) of Kahiki. Thus, Haumea is the great-grandmother of Kamapuaʻa.

By this genealogy, Pele is the senior relative of Kamapuaʻa, making her the stronger, more powerful *Akua.* By Hawaiian reckoning, their close genealogy makes them perfect and perhaps inevitable candidates for mating. The more closely related the couple, the higher the rank of the child produced (Kameʻeleihiwa 1992:40–41). When Kamapuaʻa makes love to Pele (no doubt using techniques gleaned from the Tahitian sisters), when he conquers her with his virility, he elevates himself to her level of *Akua.* He becomes a great God himself.

Similarly, when he seduces Kapo, forcing her to reattach or put on her vagina and thus submit to the physical demands of her *maʻi lele,* Kamapuaʻa conquers her *mana* and takes her knowledge as well. Kapo is famous as a Goddess of *ʻanāʻanā,* the prayers that can cause death or restore life to one who has died. Pele's younger sister Hiʻiaka uses *ʻanāʻanā* to bring Lohiʻau, Pele's lover, back to life. Kamapuaʻa uses similar prayers to revive his dead brother Kekeleiʻaikū.

No wonder Kamapuaʻa takes no time to dally with Waihīnano and the *moʻo* woman of Paukūkalo. He has no need of their power. He has already gained enough from the female side of his family, from his grandmother Kamaunuaniho, and from his cousins Pele and Kapo. He has also gained the power of second sight, or *ʻike pāpālua,* given to those with *kinolau* (many body forms) or *kinolua* (double body forms). He can see the variant body forms of different *Akua* at once, no matter what physical manifestation they may be wearing.

When Kamaunuaniho composes a name chant for Kamapuaʻa (Issue 5), she enumerates the various bodies available to him should need arise. Whenever it is chanted, Kamapuaʻa magically receives extraordinary strength and power, as exemplified by his escape from the warriors of ʻOlopana, and changes his body form. It is the combined power of the spoken word (Elbert and Mahoe 1970:19) and of *kinolau* that ensures his success or, as when Pele reveals his name chant, causes him to revert to his pig form and bellow out. It was rare for a name chant to be widely known outside of one's family, and Pele's knowledge of it implies a familial relationship. That is how she knows him so well.

The intimate recounting of the affair between Kamapuaʻa and Pele reveals the ancient struggle for dominance between man and woman, where sexual attraction is often used as a calculated advantage by both sides. At the beginning of any love affair, the man is attracted to the woman (or vice versa) but faces the possibility of rejection at their first encounter. Some would argue that Pele first tempted Kamapuaʻa in Tahiti, repeatedly sending her smoke to burn his eyes, disturbing his conjugal bliss and making it impossible for him to ignore her. It is her smoke that fetches him, and it is her challenge that lures him to her.

Pele's people, and the women who take her side, would deny the suggestion; she never sent any smoke from Kīlauea to Tahiti. The implication is absurd and merely a lie told by the pig to deceive his Tahitian sweethearts. From the female point of view, he is not a man to be trusted.

When Kamapua'a goes to the edge of the volcano (Pele's *ma'i*), he knows that he is tempting fate and may be killed in battle. Pele is a fierce and divine woman, famous for having killed her previous lover Lohi'au (Emerson 1915:208). Kamapua'a knows this—his grandmother has forewarned him that his pig bristles may be burned—but he is all the more titillated by the challenge of a dangerous encounter with a powerful woman.

Kamapua'a begins the seduction peacefully enough, sweetly chanting for Pele and her sisters to awaken. He wears his most handsome virile body in their honor, but these are Goddesses not mere Tahitian chiefesses, and they do not faint at his feet at first sight of his beauty. When Pele's sisters exalt his charms, she becomes angry and denounces him as nothing but a pig (Issue 10). The female audience applauds Pele for her astute analysis, perhaps remembering their own acquaintances with handsome piglike men. The men, hearing Pele's taunt, sympathize with the pig for his troubles in dealing with a "difficult" woman. Perhaps Pele was angry because Kamapua'a had been seen first by her sisters, precluding Pele from engaging in a brief and discrete, but satisfying, affair with him. Or perhaps she had simply had her fill of inferior, piglike men invading the privacy of her sacred mountain.

In the ensuing battle, neither side wins definitively, but the stratagems employed by each are as humorous and melodramatic as those exhibited by potential lovers who are sexually attracted despite seemingly insurmountable differences. They know they are bad for each other, but they are tempted nonetheless.

Finally, when Pele's molten lava drives Kamapua'a into the sea and he eludes her with his fish form, her anger subsides and she regrets perhaps having been too cruel to "our *kāne*" (Issue 15). Having driven him to the brink of death, and perceiving there is a chance that he might escape, she perversely wants him as a lover and will do anything, including exposing her most private parts, to lure him back. She wants him desperately, and her desire has been fueled by his nimble ability to dodge her persistent attempts to kill him.

How quickly war and anger turn to desire. She wants to taste his beautiful body even though she *knows* he is pig. The male audience laughs because even a great Goddess is not immune to the sexual temptations of a virile Hawaiian man.

Despite her assurances, when Kamapua'a returns to Kīlauea he is wary of Pele's moody disposition. His war strategist grandfather, Kūliaikekaua, warns him that when he enters the pit, he should not lose his head over the lovely young women but should choose the mature, and thus more powerful, woman, lest she kill him in anger. Pele tests him by wearing her old woman body, announcing that her *maʻi* is too old and dry to make love and urging him to take one of her beautiful younger sisters for his pleasure. When Kamapuaʻa replies that he did not "swim across the great sea" from Tahiti for them but for Pele alone (Issue 16), the women hearing this story all sigh with approbation. Perhaps he is a man who can be trusted after all.

So Pele dresses in her most alluring nubile young body and invites Kamapuaʻa "into the house." As a male pig who wishes to dominate women, he demands that they make love in the open for all to see, and upon the rough lava floor; Pele is too far gone in her desire to deny him. As the exhibitionist pig continues their lovemaking for four days and nights, the relatives gather and predict the death of Pele. She may be a Goddess, but as they say in the Hawaiian countryside, "she no can handle." His family is embarrassed but asks, what else can one expect from a pig? Kamapuaʻa has won this round of the battle with Pele, and the male audience cheers.

To save Pele, her family sends for the *maʻi lele* of her younger sister Kapo, who lives on Māui. Note that Kapo is none too eager to save Pele and makes the messengers linger awhile. By the time her *maʻi* arrives, Pele and Kamapuaʻa have already made their terms of separation, dividing the island between them with boundaries that neither should cross (Issue 17). (This arrangement would sound familiar to many a divorced couple.) Their child, however, indicates in Hawaiian terms that there is an eternal bond between them and elevates the genealogical status of Kamapuaʻa to that of a full-fledged *Akua* like Pele.

Kapo, on the other hand, is an entirely different woman. She maintains strict control over her sexual desires, taking them off, wrapping them in *kapa,* and leaving them undisturbed in the corner. When she hears of Pele's troubles, she deliberately sends her *maʻi lele* to lure Kamapuaʻa away from her older sister, proving to all that her flying vagina is more desirable and more capable than that of the fire Goddess. This is a contest between sisters; it is also a competition between *Akua* of Māui and *Akua* of the island of Hawaiʻi.

Kapo is not afraid; she is eager to find a man who can satisfy her sexual appetite and provide her with sufficient reason to wear her *maʻi* once more. Nor does she make it easy for him to ensnare her. Her *maʻi* flies from Kīlauea to Hilo to Hāmākua to Kohala, and then across the channel to Māui. At each stop, as soon as he arrives hoping to enjoy her, she flies away again, all to fuel his sexual frustration. She reels him in like a fish on a hook. The female audience cheers. Kapo becomes the champion *wahine* who will put that pig in his place.

However, when Kamapuaʻa finally arrives at Kapo's house in Wailua, he feigns fatigue. She is ready and eagerly invites him to enter "the house"

(Issue 18). He makes her wait, teasing her a little, claiming he must catch his breath. It is the eternal nature of men to make a woman wait when she is ready, and Kapo enjoys him more because of it.

In his usual charming manner, Kamapua'a pauses to gaze upon her loveliness and tell her that she is "the most beautiful woman of the Ko'olau cliffs of Māui." She teases him by agreeing that she is lovely above, but tells him there is nothing down below. With his powers of second sight, he spots the *ma'i lele* hidden in the corner and induces her to put it on. At last, nothing can stop the pig from fulfilling his desire.

For her part, Kapo is entirely enthralled with the inexhaustible prowess of the pig. When her former *kāne* with the "big flower" tries to interfere with their lovemaking, Kapo blithely agrees that Kamapua'a should toss him away to the mountains. She has no regrets. At last she has found the perfect mate, the one man who can satisfy her sexual desires. Who then has won the battle? Kapo will not die from excessive lovemaking as Pele threatened to do. It seems that Kapo has bested the pig but, as the men suspect, not for long.

After twenty days, Kapo maintains her unrestrained delight with Kamapua'a and is perhaps planning for them to live together "forever." Kamapua'a shuns entanglement, insisting that he must hurry away to the rescue of his dead brother. Family in Hawai'i traditionally is more important than any lover, but this is a flimsy excuse because his brother has been dead a long time, since even before he made love to Pele.

Kapo is tormented by the thought of his leaving and squirms back and forth all night, seeking an acceptable alternative. Every woman has played this scene with her man, and can empathize. Finally, in the morning, she tosses aside all pride and begs him to stay (Issue 19). Kamapua'a is coldly adamant about leaving immediately, but he relents a little to ease the tension. He condescends to permit her to follow him after a passage of time, but only if she still loves him, and he does not even tell her where to search for him.

What kind of man behaves in such a heartless manner? Only a pig! She accepts his terms and vows to "swim the vast sea" for him. What kind of a woman accepts such terms? Only a woman whose sexual desires must be satisfied by a pig! Kamapua'a, after all, is not just any pig. "His bearing was that of one glorious and beyond compare, the type that is flocked after by youth, and cherished by the gentle sex" (Issue 20).

This story seems to be a warning to women everywhere, but especially in Hawai'i, to guard their hearts against such gorgeous and dangerously tempting men, whose handsome beauty will make a woman think with her *ma'i* instead of her brain. Perhaps the *Ka Leo o ka Lāhui* version of the Kamapua'a epic was written by a woman. (Was S. Pa'aluhi a female?)

A final implication in the *moʻolelo* is the role of Pele and Kamapuaʻa as possible female and male symbols for the common, everyday Hawaiian of traditional Hawaiʻi. Which heroines and heroes did Hawaiians emulate in their personal lives? The character traits of Pele were exciting and worthy of emulation; she was one of the most powerful female Hawaiian *Akua*. She is at once loving and spiteful, a young beauty and an old hag, divine and human, omnipotent but erring in judgment; it is she who devours and scorches the countryside while creating and giving birth to new land. Scorning Kamapuaʻa as a pig, she relents to take him as her lover. A proud woman, always equal to her lovers, she would be a grand yet familiar model for any Hawaiian woman.

Kamapuaʻa, as we have seen, is the virile young champion, the ferocious, "rooting" pig. His motto seems to have been Love Them and Leave Them, as the daughters of Koea, Pele, and even Kapo so rudely discover. At the very moment when these women fall hopelessly in love with him, when their seduction is truly complete, his desire is fulfilled and he departs for new adventures. Might he not have been the Hawaiian male prototype?

Hawaiian society was marked by its lack of formal marriage ceremonies, long-term monogamous relationships (Malo 1951:74), and strict observance of nuclear families. Partners were exchanged at will, sexual favors were considered a courtesy, and children were raised collectively by an extended family (Pukui, Haertig, and Lee 1972:75–120). All of this is celebrated by the infamous love affair of Hawaiian literature, that of Pele and Kamapuaʻa, where Kamapuaʻa tries to flood Pele's pit and extinguish her fires, metaphorically attempting to quench the fire of her desire without being overcome by that fire, only to abandon her for her more tempting sister. What else can we expect from a pig?

As in the antithetical balance evident in all Hawaiian thought, the world revolves upon opposition: darkness and light; rain and sun; sea and earth; sacred and profane; male and female; Kū, the *Akua* of war, and Lono, the *Akua* of peace; Pele, the *Akua* of destruction, and Kamapuaʻa, the *Akua* of lush vegetation. This union of opposites creates the world.

LITERATURE CITED

Alexander, William D. 1896. *History of the Later Years of the Hawaiian Monarchy . . . and the Revolution of* 1893. Honolulu: Hawaiian Gazette Co.

Alpers, Antony. 1987. *The World of the Polynesians, Seen Through Their Myths and Legends, Poetry and Art.* Auckland: Oxford University Press.

Andrews, Lorrin. 1865. *A Dictionary of the Hawaiian Language.* Honolulu: H. M. Whitney. Reprinted in 1974 by Charles E. Tuttle Company, Japan.

Andrews, Lorrin, and Henry H. Parker. 1922. *A Dictionary of the Hawaiian Language.* Revised by Henry H. Parker. Honolulu: Board of Commissioners of the Public Archives of the Territory of Hawaii.

Beckwith, Martha Warren. 1919. "The Hawaiian Romance of Laieikawai" [by S. N. Haleole, 1863], with introduction and translation. Washington, D.C.: Bureau of American Ethnology Annual Report 33 (for 1911–1912), 285–677.

Beckwith, Martha Warren. 1932. *Kepelino's Traditions of Hawaii.* Bernice Pauahi Bishop Museum Bulletin 95. Honolulu: Bishop Museum Press.

Beckwith, Martha Warren. 1970. *Hawaiian Mythology.* Honolulu: University of Hawai'i Press. (First published in 1940 by Yale University Press.)

Beckwith, Martha Warren, ed. 1972. *The Kumulipo.* Honolulu: University of Hawai'i Press. (Originally published in 1951 by University of Chicago Press.)

Bier, James Allen. 1977. *Map of Moloka'i, The Friendly Isle.* Honolulu: University of Hawai'i Press.

Bier, James Allen. 1987. *Map of O'ahu, The Gathering Place.* Honolulu: University of Hawai'i Press.

Bier, James Allen. 1988. *Map of Hawai'i, The Big Island.* Honolulu: University of Hawai'i Press.

Bier, James Allen. 1988. *Map of Maui, The Valley Isle.* Honolulu: University of Hawai'i Press.

Bier, James Allen. 1991. *Map of Kaua'i, The Garden Isle.* Honolulu: University of Hawai'i Press.

Bush, John E., and S. Pa'aluhi. 1893. "Hi'iaka-i-ka-poli-o-Pele." *Ka Leo o ka Lāhui.* January 5.

Cummins, John A. 1913. "Around O'ahu in Days of Old." In *Mid-Pacific Magazine*. Vol. 6, No. 3, pp. 233–43.

Dibble, Sheldon. 1843. *A History of the Sandwich Islands.* Reissued in 1909 by Thomas Thrum, Honolulu.

Elbert, Samuel H. 1976. "Connotative Values of Hawaiian Place Names." In: A. L. Kaeppler and H. A. Nimmo, eds., *Directions in Pacific Traditional Literature,* 117–33. Bernice Pauahi Bishop Museum Special Publication 62. Honolulu: Bishop Museum Press.

Elbert, Samuel H., and Noelani K. Mahoe. 1970. *Na Mele o Hawai'i Nei: 101 Songs of Hawai'i.* Honolulu: University of Hawai'i Press.

Emerson, Nathaniel B. 1909. *Unwritten Literature of Hawaii: The Sacred Songs of the Hula.* Smithsonian Institution Bureau of American Ethnology Bulletin 38. Washington, D.C.: Government Printing Office.

Emerson, Nathaniel B. 1915. *Pele and Hiiaka: A Myth from Hawaii.* Honolulu: Star Bulletin Limited.

Fornander, Abraham. 1916–1920. *Fornander Collection of Hawaiian Antiquities and Folklore.* Vols. IV, V, and VI. Honolulu: Bishop Museum Press.

Green, Laura C. S. 1923. *Hawaiian Stories and Wise Sayings.* Edited by Martha W. Beckwith. Poughkeepsie, N.Y.: Vassar College.

Handy, Craighill E. S., and Elizabeth Green Handy. 1972. *Native Planters in Old Hawaii.* Bernice Pauahi Bishop Museum Bulletin 233. Honolulu: Bishop Museum Press.

Henry, Teuira. 1985. Reprint of the original 1928 edition. *Ancient Tahiti.* Honolulu: Bishop Museum Press.

Ii, John Papa. 1959. *Fragments of Hawaiian History.* Mary K. Pukui, trans.; Dorothy B. Barrère, ed. Honolulu: Bishop Museum Press.

Indices of Awards Made by the Board of Commissioners to Quiet Land Titles in the Hawaiian Islands. 1929. Honolulu: Star-Bulletin Press.

The Islander. 1875. A weekly journal. Honolulu: Thomas G. Thrum. March 5–October 29.

Judd, Henry P. 1930. *Hawaiian Proverbs and Riddles.* Bernice Pauahi Bishop Museum Bulletin 77. Honolulu: Bishop Museum Press.

Kahiolo, G. W. 1978. *He Moolelo no Kamapua'a.* Text from *Ka Hae Hawaii,*

1861. Translated by Esther Moʻokini, Erin Neizman, and David Tom. Honolulu: Hawaiian Studies Program.

Kaʻimikaua, John. 1979. "Some Stories about Kamapuaʻa." A lecture for Religion 482B, University of Hawaii. September 27.

Kamakau, Samuel M. 1867. "Ka Moolelo o Kamehameha I." *Ka Nupepa Kuokoa,* January 12.

Kamakau, Samuel M. 1870. "Ka Moolelo o Hawaii." *Ke Au Okoa,* March 31, May 19, July 14.

Kamakau, Samuel M. 1961. *Ruling Chiefs of Hawaii.* Honolulu: Kamehameha Schools Press. (Originally published in 1867 in *Ka Nupepa Kuokoa.*)

Kamakau, Samuel M. 1964. *Ka Poʻe Kahiko: The People of Old.* Mary K. Pukui, trans., Dorothy B. Barrère, ed. Bernice Pauahi Bishop Museum Special Publication 5. Honolulu: Bishop Museum Press.

Kamakau, Samuel M. 1976. *The Works of the People of Old: Na Hana a ka Poʻe Kahiko.* Mary K. Pukui, trans., Dorothy B. Barrère, ed. Bernice Pauahi Bishop Museum Special Publication 61. Honolulu: Bishop Museum Press.

Kamakau, Samuel M. 1991. *Nā Moʻolelo a ka Poʻe Kahiko: The Traditions of the People of Old.* Honolulu: Bishop Museum Press.

Kameʻeleihiwa, Lilikalā. 1992. *Native Land and Foreign Desires: Pehea Lā E Pono Ai?* Honolulu: Bishop Museum Press.

Kanakaʻole, Edith K. 1978. "The Nature of ʻOhana." A lecture for Chant 11. St. Louis High School. Honolulu. June 28.

Kauakahiakahaola, S.M.K. 1875. "He Manawa haowale anei keia, a Kaili a pakaha wale?" *Ka Nupepa Kuokoa,* November 27.

Kirtley, Bacil. 1971. *A Motif–Index of Traditional Polynesian Narratives.* Honolulu: University of Hawaiʻi Press.

Kuykendall, Ralph S. 1967. *The Hawaiian Kingdom.* Volume III, *The Kalakaua Dynasty 1874–1893.* Honolulu: University of Hawaiʻi Press.

Luomala, Katharine. 1965. "Creative Processes in Hawaiian Use of Place Names in Chant." Reprint from *Laographia,* Vol. 22, pp. 234–37.

Malo, David. 1951. *Hawaiian Antiquities.* Nathaniel B. Emerson, trans. Bernice Pauahi Bishop Museum Special Publication 2. Honolulu: Bishop Museum Press.

McAllister, J. Gilbert. 1933. *Archaeology of Oahu.* Bernice Pauahi Bishop Museum Bulletin 104. Honolulu: Bishop Museum Press.

Nakuina, Moses. n.d. *Moʻolelo Hawaii o Pakaʻa a me Kua-a-Pakaa, Na Kahu Iwikuamoʻo o Keawenuiaumi, Ke Alii o Hawaii, ao na Moʻopuna Hoi A LAAMAOMAO!* Honolulu: n.p.

Naliʻiʻelua, Kalāhikiola. 1979. "Kamapuaʻa." A lecture for Religion 482B, University of Hawaii. December 4.

Palikoʻolauloa, M. K. 1861. "Na Wahi Pana o Kaliuwaʻa." *Ka Hoku o ka Pakipika*, November 14.

Pukui, Mary Kawena. 1983. *ʻŌlelo Noʻeau*. Bernice Pauahi Bishop Museum Special Publication 71. Honolulu: Bishop Museum Press.

Pukui, Mary Kawena, and Samuel H. Elbert. 1971. *Hawaiian Dictionary*. Honolulu: University of Hawaiʻi Press.

Pukui, Mary Kawena, Samuel H. Elbert, and Esther T. Mookini. 1974. *Place Names of Hawaii*. Revised and expanded edition. Honolulu: University of Hawaiʻi Press.

Pukui, Mary Kawena, E. W. Haertig, and Catherine A. Lee. 1972. *Nānā i ke Kumu*. Vol. II. Honolulu: Queen Liliʻuokalani Children's Center.

Rice, William Hyde. 1923. *Hawaiian Legends*. Bernice Pauahi Bishop Museum Bulletin 3. Honolulu: Bishop Museum Press.

Sahlins, Marshall D. 1981. *Historical Metaphors and Mythical Realities: Structure in the Early History of the Sandwich Islands Kingdom*. Ann Arbor: University of Michigan Press.

Sahlins, Marshall D. 1985. *Islands of History*. Chicago: University of Chicago Press.

Schmitt, Robert C. 1968. *Demographic Statistics of Hawaii, 1778–1965*. Honolulu: University of Hawaiʻi Press.

Stannard, David E. 1989. *Before the Horror: The Population of Hawaiʻi on the Eve of Western Contact*. Honolulu: SSRI, University of Hawaiʻi.

Sterling, Elspeth P., and Catherine C. Summers. 1978. *Sites of Oʻahu*. Honolulu: Bernice Pauahi Bishop Museum.

Thrum, Thomas George. 1907. *Hawaiian Folk Tales: A Collection of Native Legends*. Chicago: A. C. McClung & Co.

Turner, George L.L.P. 1984. Reprint of the original 1884 edition. *Samoa, A Hundred Years Ago and Long Before*. Suva: University of the South Pacific.

Westervelt, William Drake. 1915. *Legends of Gods and Ghosts*. Boston: George H. Ellis Co.

INDEX OF ANNOTATIONS

INDEX OF IDIOMS AND SAYINGS

nona hoʻi o Hoʻolehehekiʻi
99

ʻo Kama i ka lehua lihilihi lua
o Kaliuwaʻa 86
ʻo kaʻu ʻai kēia me kaʻu iʻa 51
ʻo ka wai huʻihuʻi o Elieli 6
ʻO nā ʻinalua iho la nō ia i
ka nuku 105

ʻO nā iwi 52, 126
ʻo na maka o kahi walewale
126

Pau ʻē nā wahi iwi ona i ka
hakihaki 26
pau ka palena ʻiliwai 110
polapola aku nā maka 105
pupuhi ka iʻa o Ukoʻa 129

Ua hele nō hoʻi a ʻai ka
manu i luna 106
ua lele mua ka eiki [keiki]
ka mea makaʻu 120
Ua loaʻa iā lāua ka lāʻau a ke
aliʻi, a Kekuaokalani 99
Ua pani ʻaweoweo ʻia ka puka
o na hale o Waiʻanae 43

INDEX OF CHANTS